LEARNING TOGETHER

ADVICE AND INSTRUCTIONS ON COMPLETING THESE TESTS

1. There are 75 questions in each test. Make sure you have not missed a page.
2. Start at question 1 and work your way to question 75.
3. If you are unable to complete a question leave it and go to the next one.
4. Do not think about the question you have just left as this wastes time.
5. If you change an answer make sure the change is clear.
6. Each test should take approximately 40 minutes.
7. When you have finished each test mark it with an adult.
8. An adult or parent may be able to explain any questions you do not understand.

TEST 01

SCORE ___________

Which two are exactly the same? Circle two letters each time.

1 A B C D E

2 A B C D E

3 A B C D E

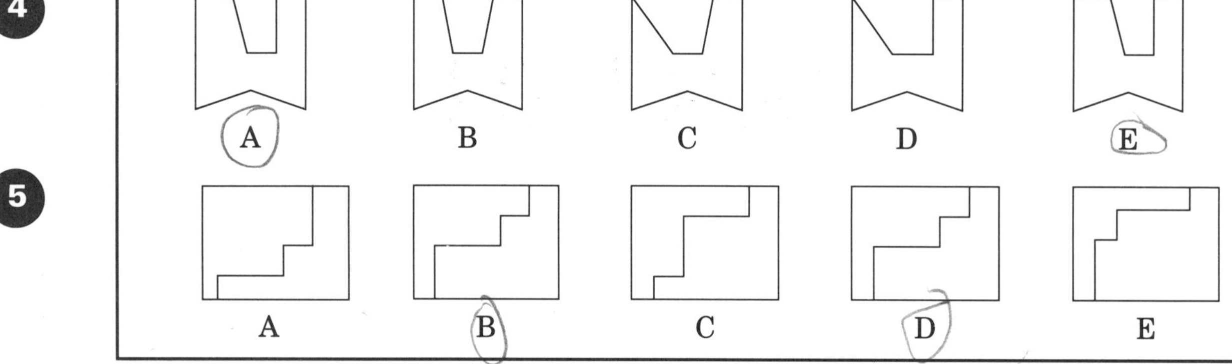

4 A B C D E

5 A B C D E

What fraction is shaded each time? Circle one answer.

6 $\frac{3}{4}$ $\frac{5}{6}$ $\frac{2}{3}$ $\frac{3}{5}$

7 $\frac{1}{4}$ $\frac{3}{8}$ $\frac{1}{3}$ $\frac{2}{5}$

8 $\frac{1}{3}$ $\frac{1}{4}$ $\frac{1}{2}$ $\frac{2}{5}$

9 $\frac{2}{3}$ $\frac{4}{7}$ $\frac{5}{8}$ $\frac{5}{6}$

10 $\frac{3}{4}$ $\frac{5}{9}$ $\frac{2}{3}$ $\frac{1}{2}$

11 $\frac{1}{4}$ $\frac{7}{12}$ $\frac{1}{3}$ $\frac{3}{8}$

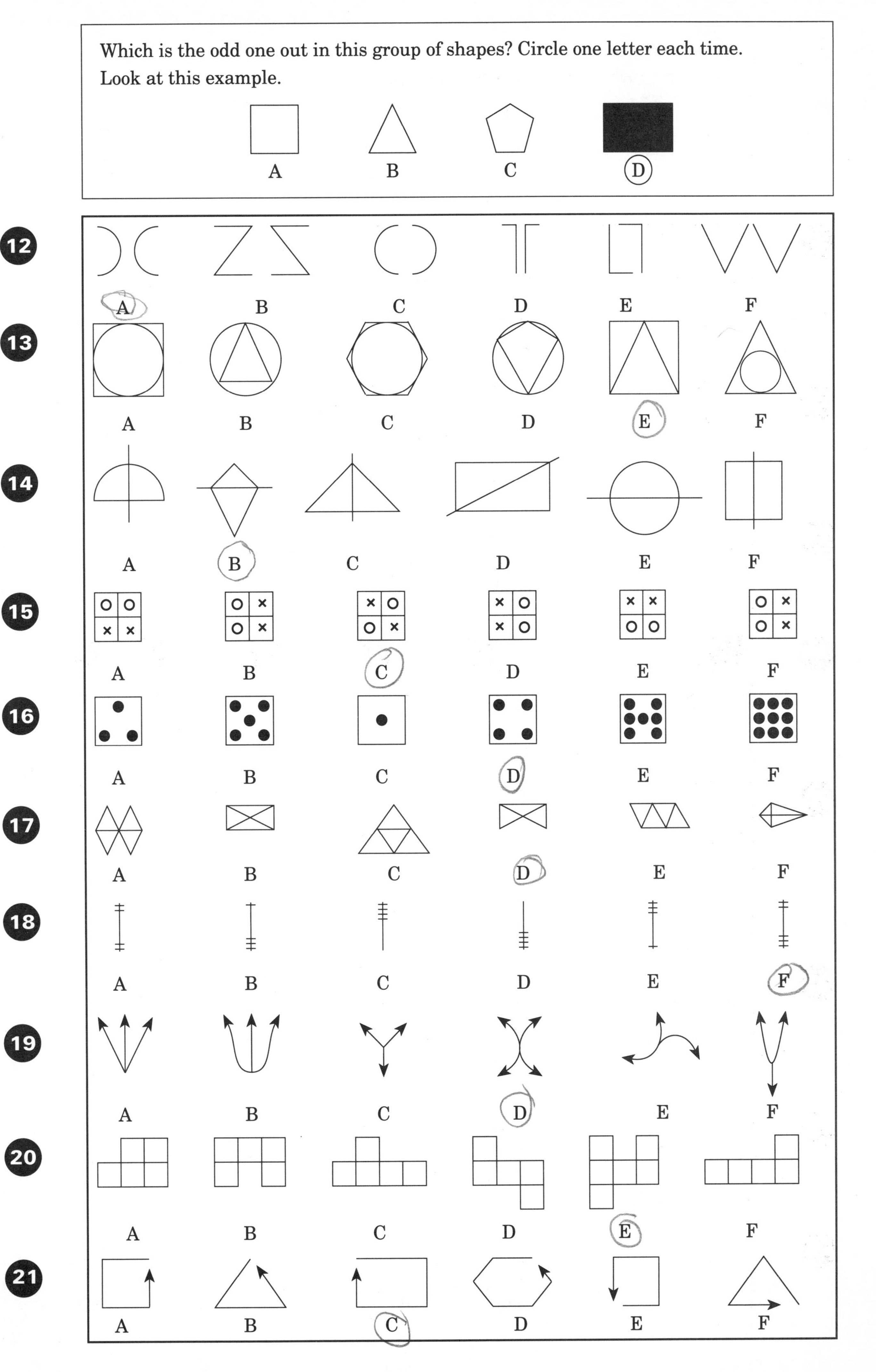
Which is the odd one out in this group of shapes? Circle one letter each time.
Look at this example.
A B C D
12
A B C D E F
13
A B C D E F
14
A B C D E F
15
A B C D E F
16
A B C D E F
17
A B C D E F
18
A B C D E F
19
A B C D E F
20
A B C D E F
21
A B C D E F

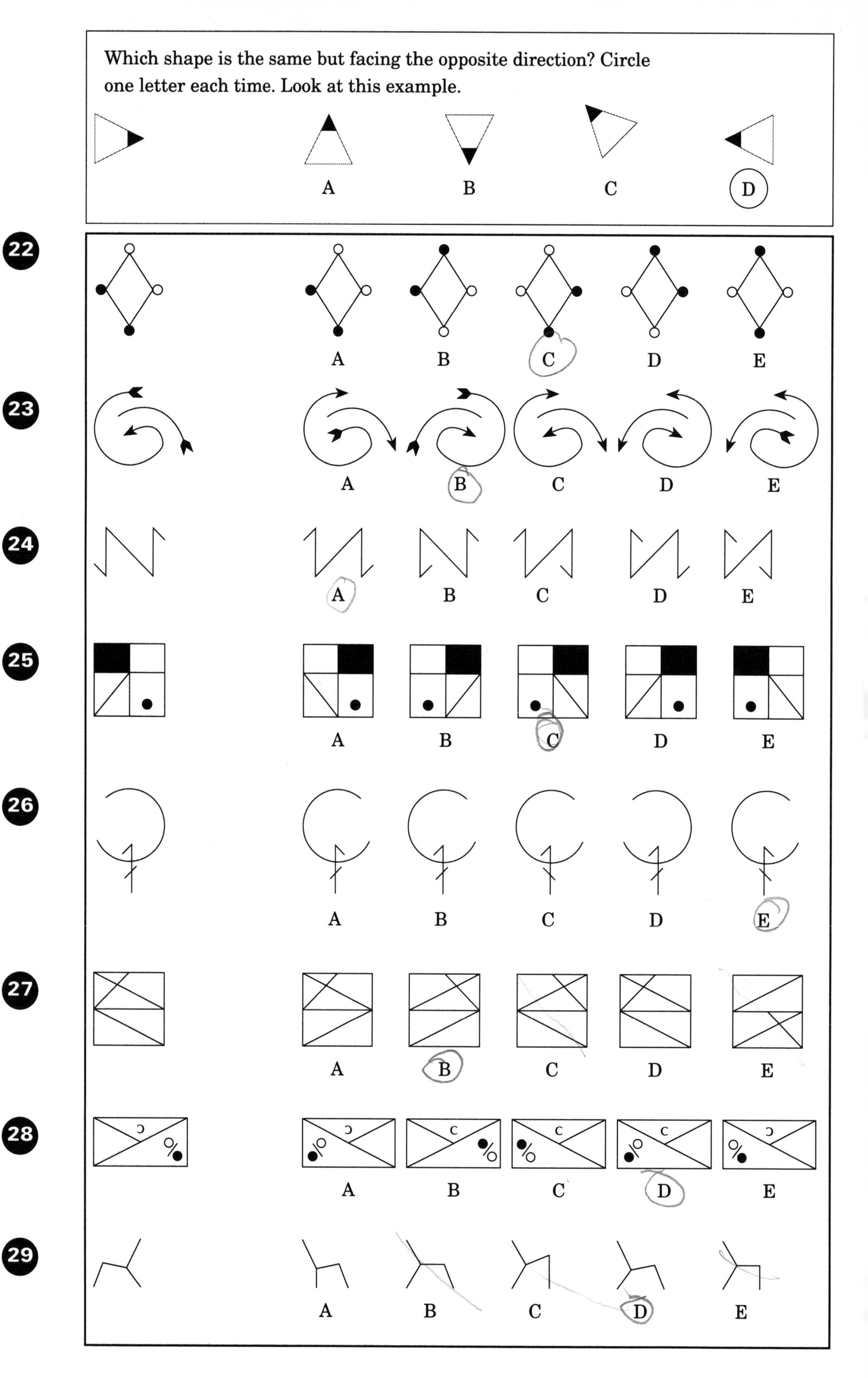
Which shape is the same but facing the opposite direction? Circle one letter each time. Look at this example.
A B C D
22
A B C D E
23
A B C D E
24
A B C D E
25
A B C D E
26
A B C D E
27
A B C D E
28
A B C D E
29
A B C D E

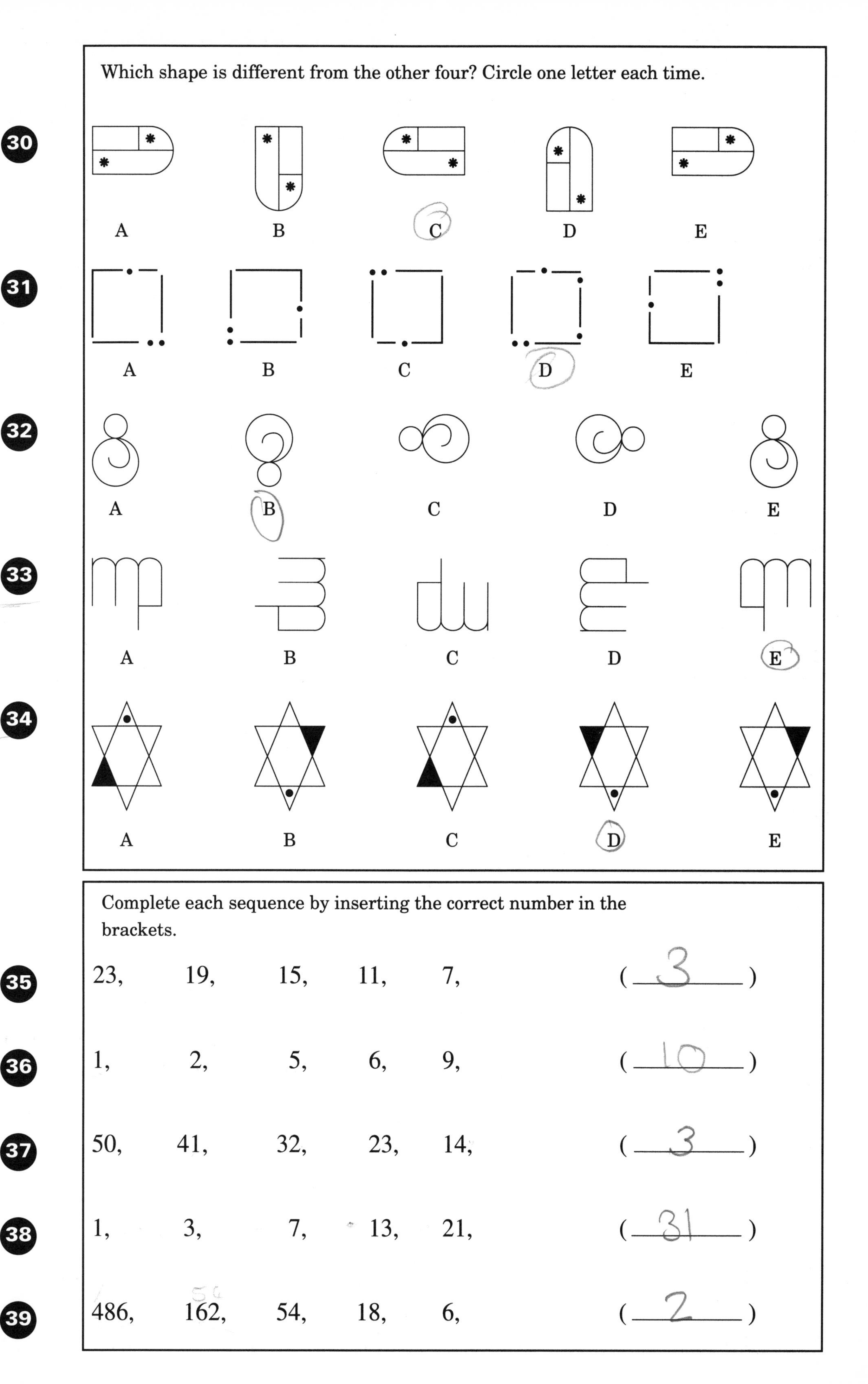

Which shape is different from the other four? Circle one letter each time.

30 A B C D E

31 A B C D E

32 A B C D E

33 A B C D E

34 A B C D E

Complete each sequence by inserting the correct number in the brackets.

35 23, 19, 15, 11, 7, (_____)

36 1, 2, 5, 6, 9, (_____)

37 50, 41, 32, 23, 14, (_____)

38 1, 3, 7, 13, 21, (_____)

39 486, 162, 54, 18, 6, (_____)

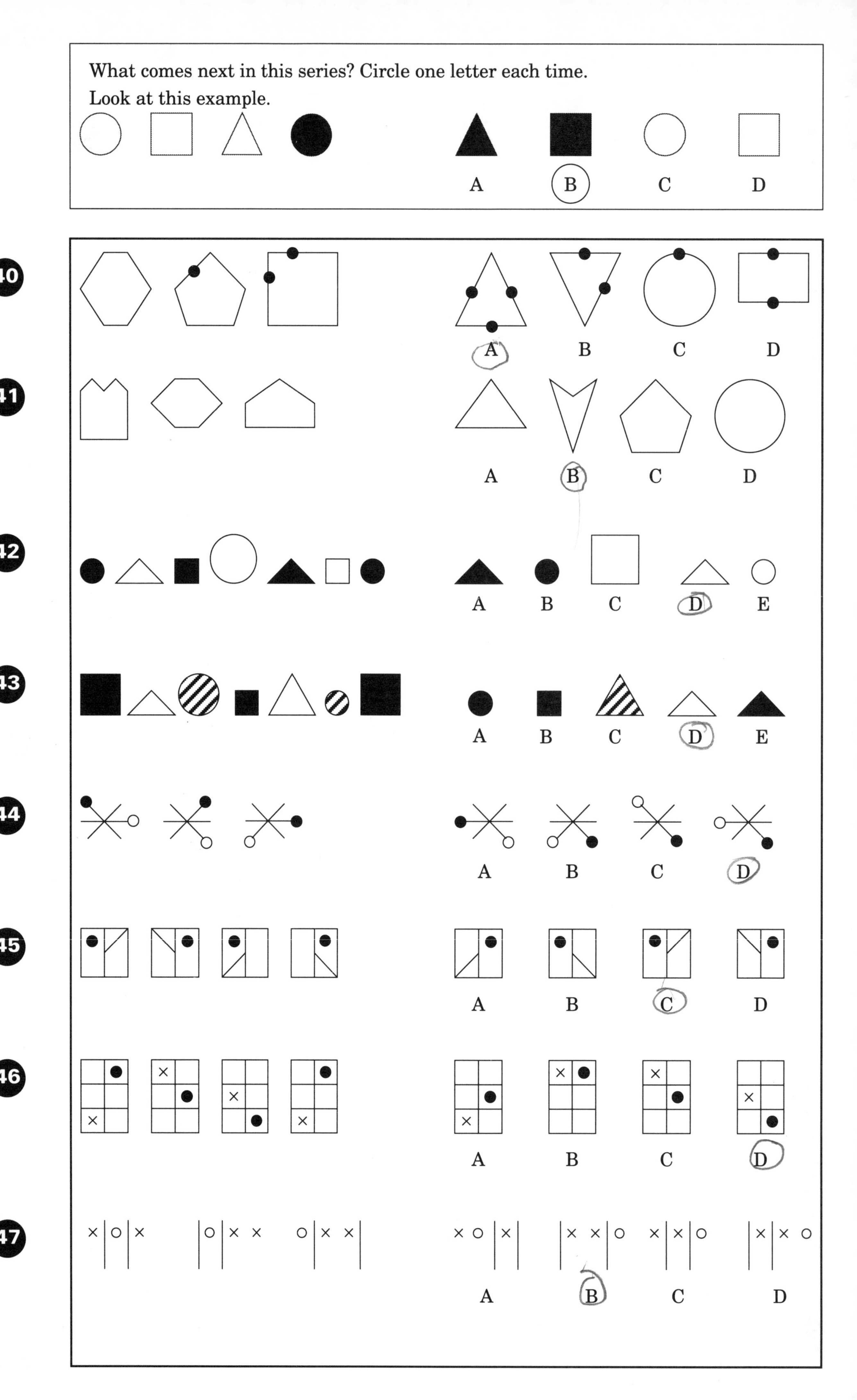
What comes next in this series? Circle one letter each time.
Look at this example.
A B C D
40
A B C D
41
A B C D
42
A B C D E
43
A B C D E
44
A B C D
45
A B C D
46
A B C D
47
A B C D

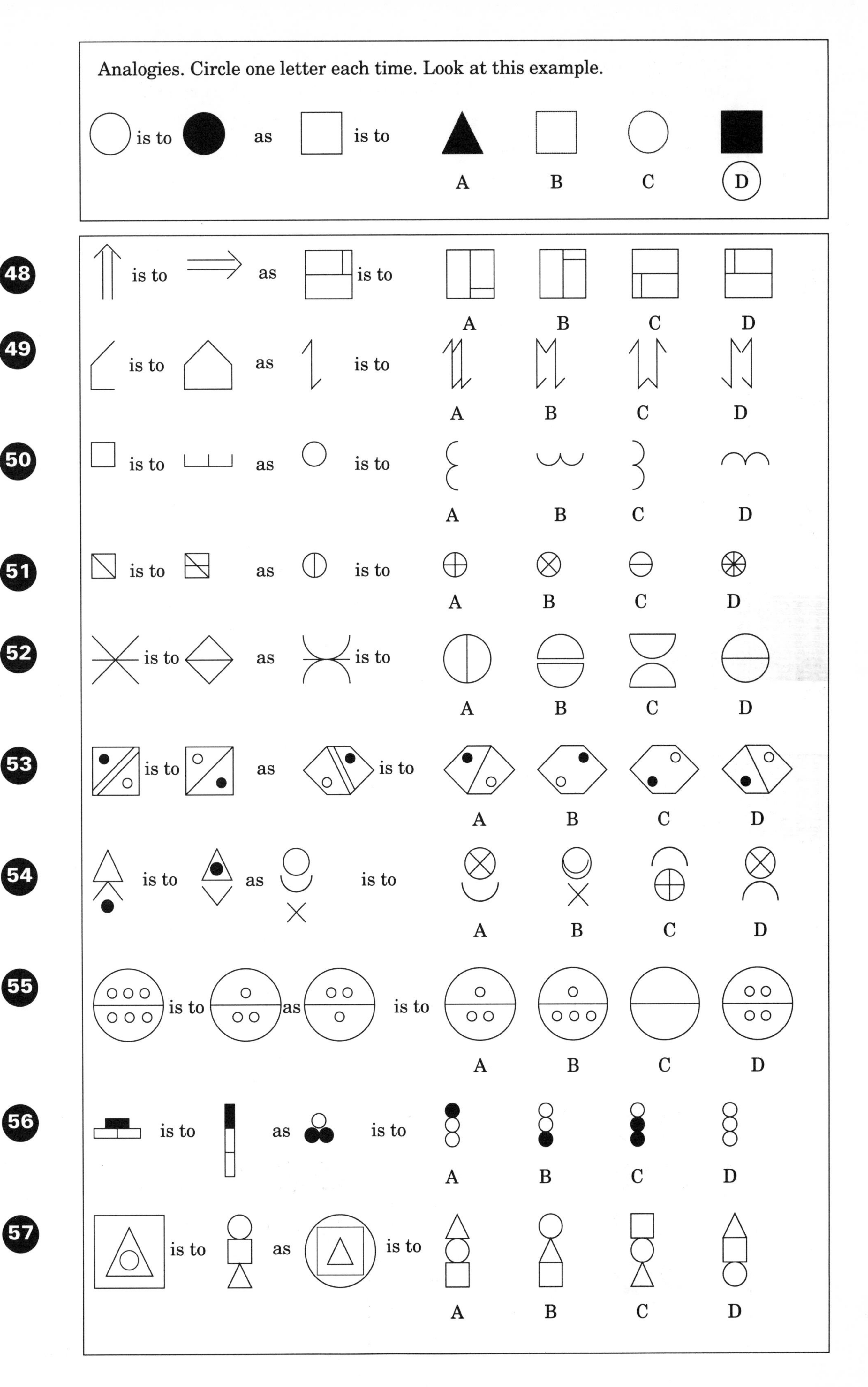
Analogies. Circle one letter each time. Look at this example.
is to
as
is to
A
B
C
D
48
is to
as
is to
A
B
C
D
49
is to
as
is to
A
B
C
D
50
is to
as
is to
A
B
C
D
51
is to
as
is to
A
B
C
D
52
is to
as
is to
A
B
C
D
53
is to
as
is to
A
B
C
D
54
is to
as
is to
A
B
C
D
55
is to
as
is to
A
B
C
D
56
is to
as
is to
A
B
C
D
57
is to
as
is to
A
B
C
D

In these questions the two shapes are either added together or subtracted from each other. The shapes do not turn. Circle one answer. Look at this example.

A (B) C D

58 A B C D

59 A B C D

60 A B C D

61 A B C D

62 A B C D

Complete this mathematical table.

63 64 65 66 67 68 69 70 71

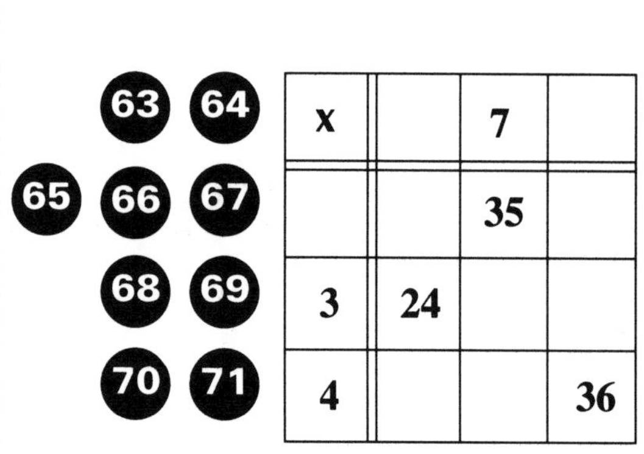

x		7	
		35	
3	24		
4			36

Supply the missing numbers in this subtraction sum.

72 73 74 75

$$\begin{array}{r} 6\ 2\ 4\ 7 \\ -\ \square\ 8\ 2\ \square \\ \hline 1\ \square\ \square\ 9 \end{array}$$

TEST 02

SCORE ____________

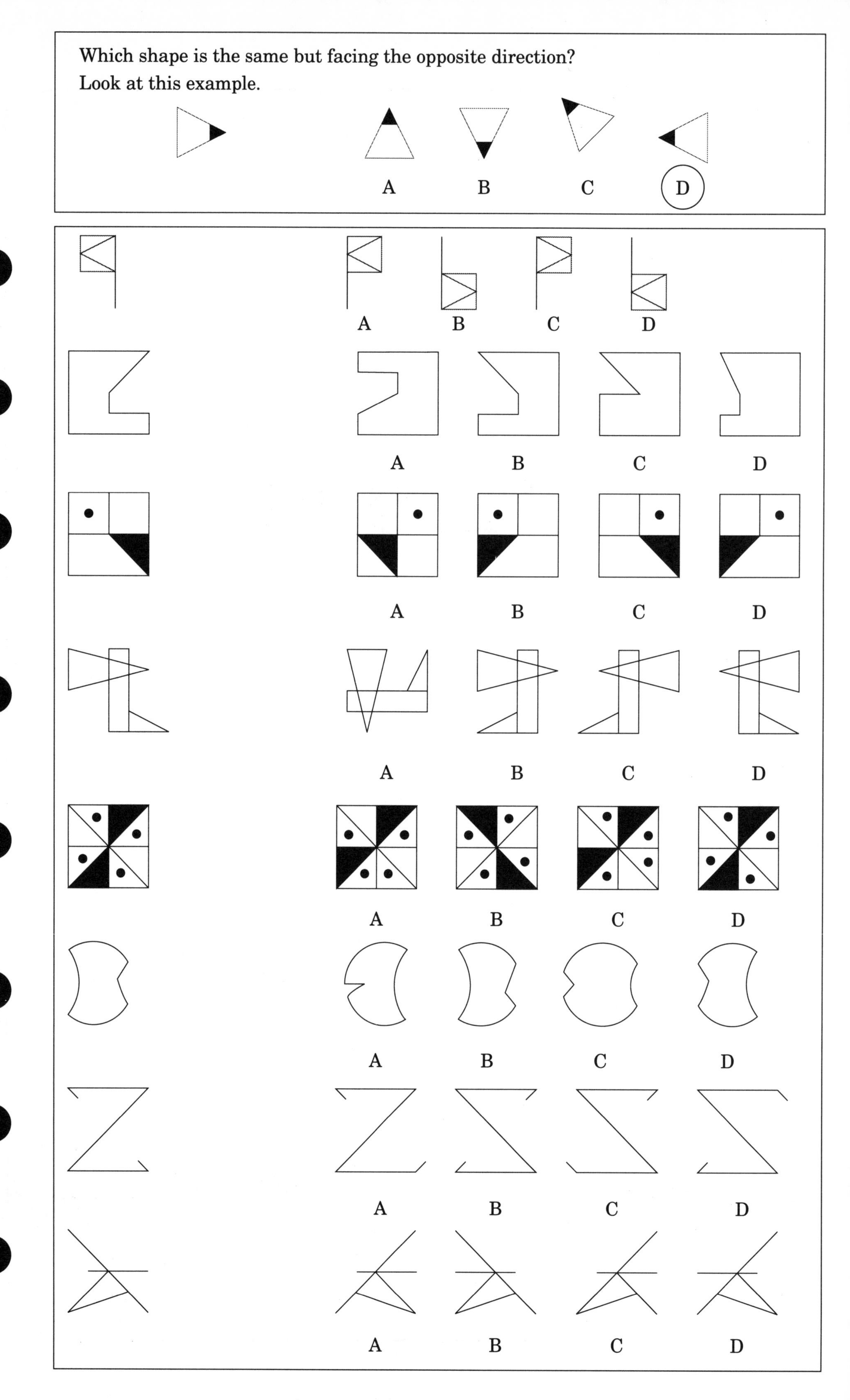
Which shape is the same but facing the opposite direction?
Look at this example.
A
B
C
D
1
A
B
C
D
2
A
B
C
D
3
A
B
C
D
4
A
B
C
D
5
A
B
C
D
6
A
B
C
D
7
A
B
C
D
8
A
B
C
D

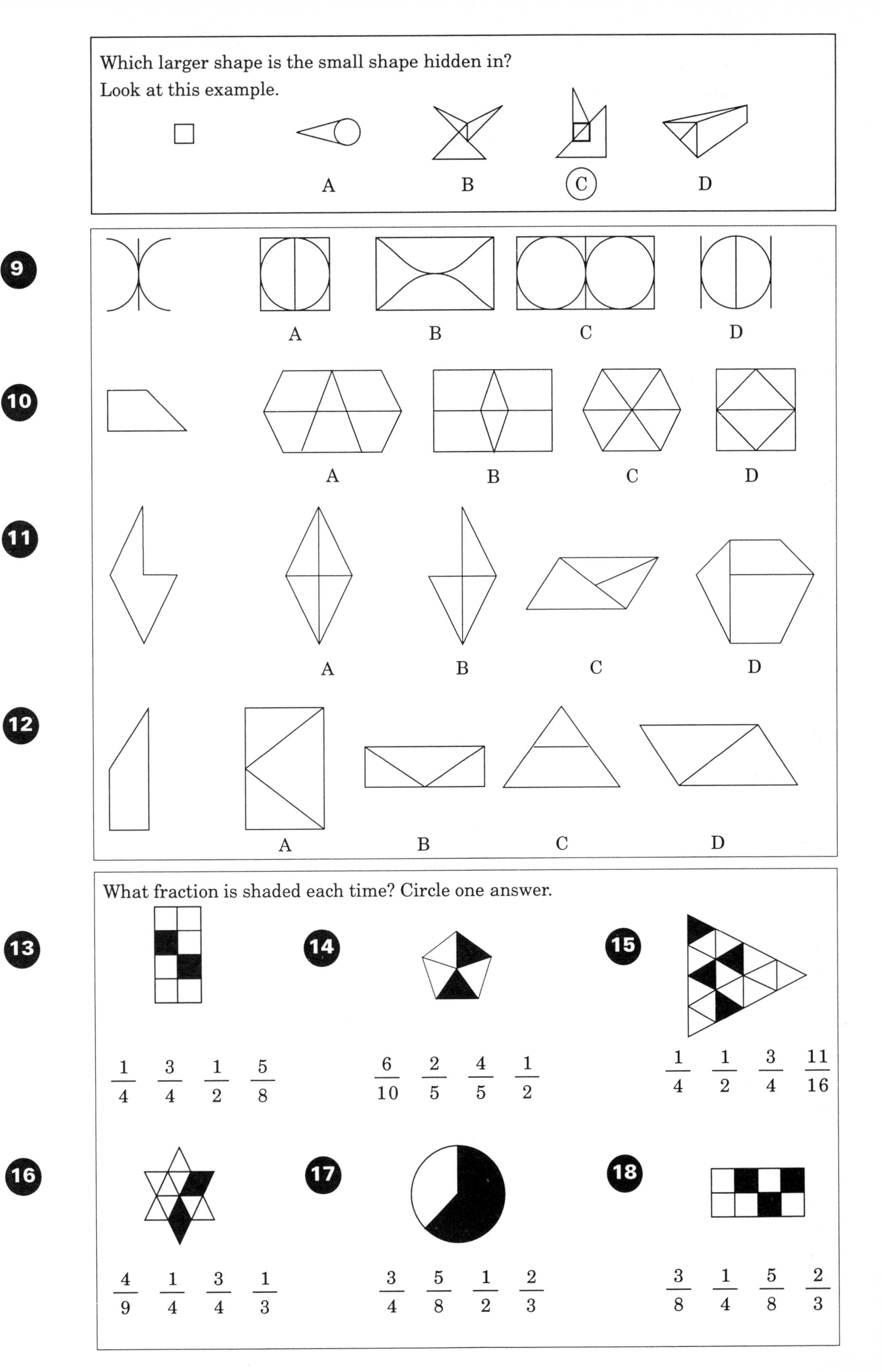

Which larger shape is the small shape hidden in?
Look at this example.
A
B
C
D
9
A
B
C
D
10
A
B
C
D
11
A
B
C
D
12
A
B
C
D
What fraction is shaded each time? Circle one answer.
13
1/4 3/4 1/2 5/8
14
6/10 2/5 4/5 1/2
15
1/4 1/2 3/4 11/16
16
4/9 1/4 3/4 1/3
17
3/4 5/8 1/2 2/3
18
3/8 1/4 5/8 2/3

In these questions the two shapes are either added together or subtracted from each other. The shapes do not turn. Circle one answer. Look at this example:

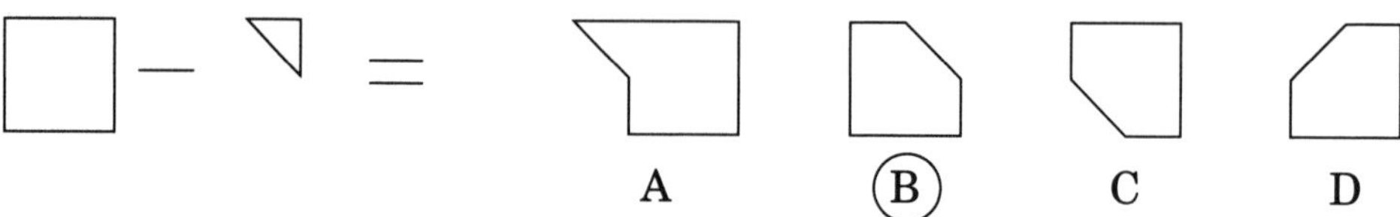

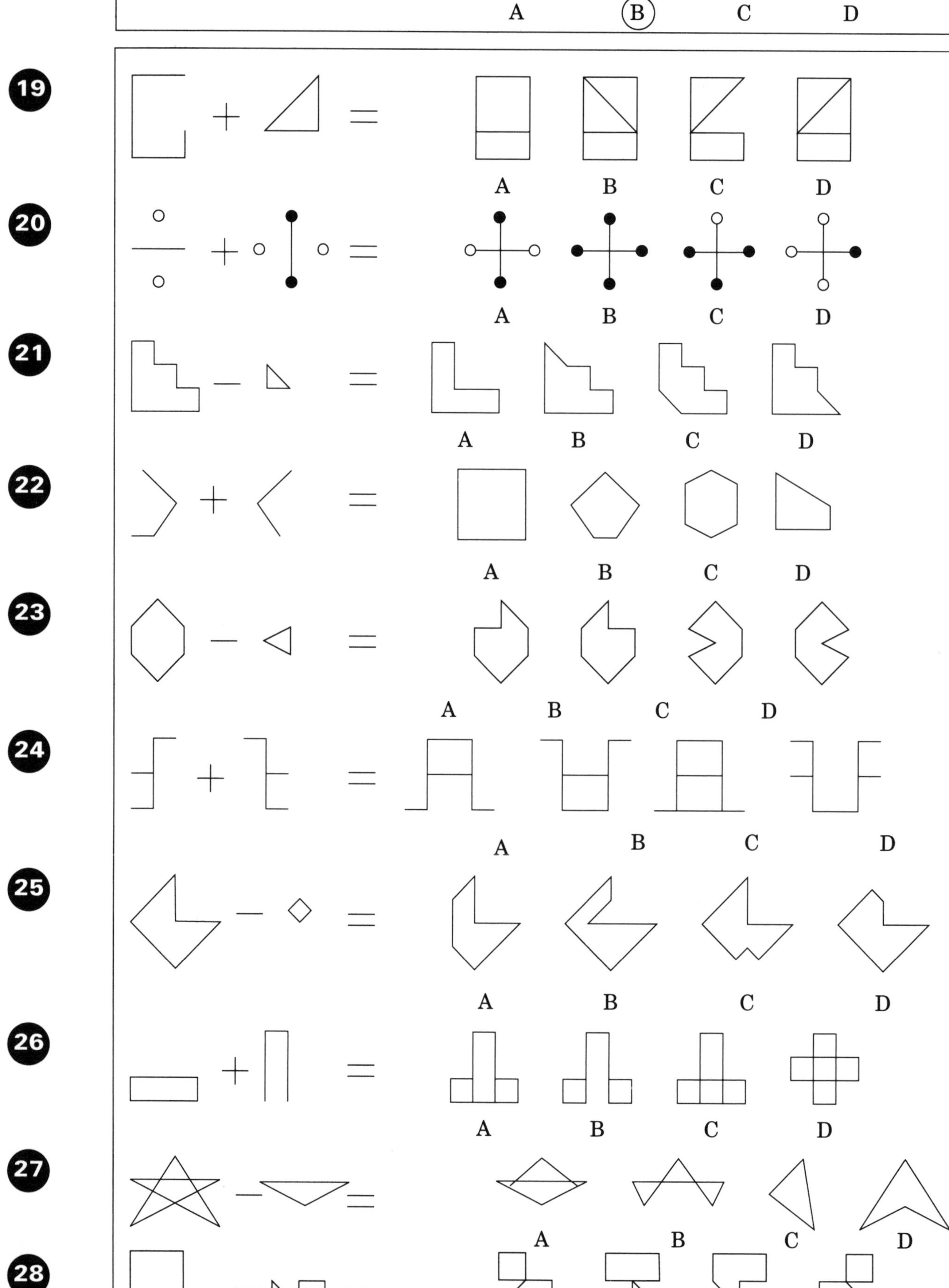

Which is the odd one out in this group of shapes? Circle one letter each time
Look at this example

A B C (D)

29 A B C D

30 A B C D

31 A B C D E

32 A B C D E

33 A B C D E

Complete this mathematical table.

34 35 36 37 38 39 40 41 42

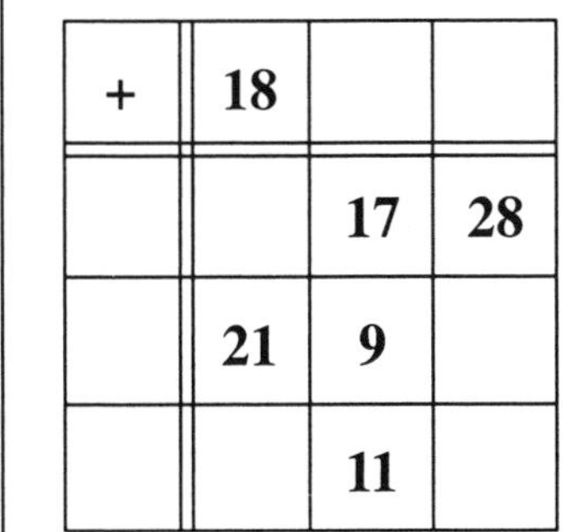

+	18		
		17	28
	21	9	
		11	

Supply the missing numbers.

43 44 45

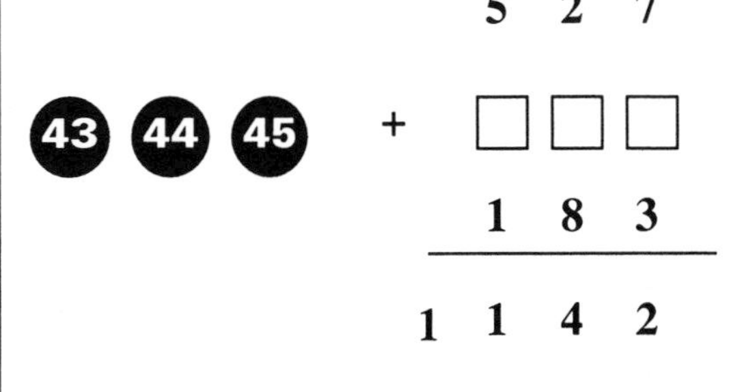

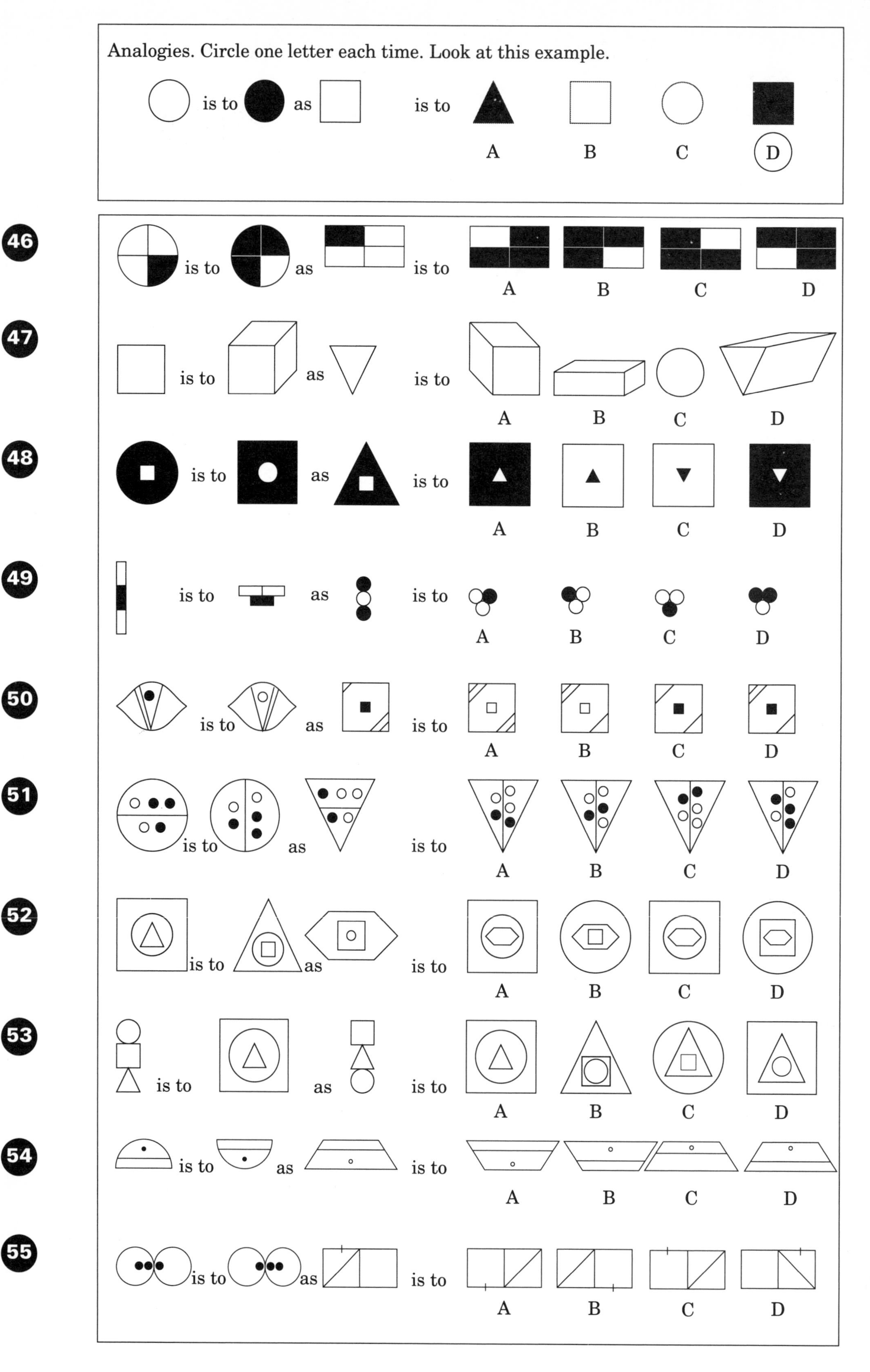
Analogies. Circle one letter each time. Look at this example.
is to
as
is to
A
B
C
D
46
47
48
49
50
51
52
53
54
55

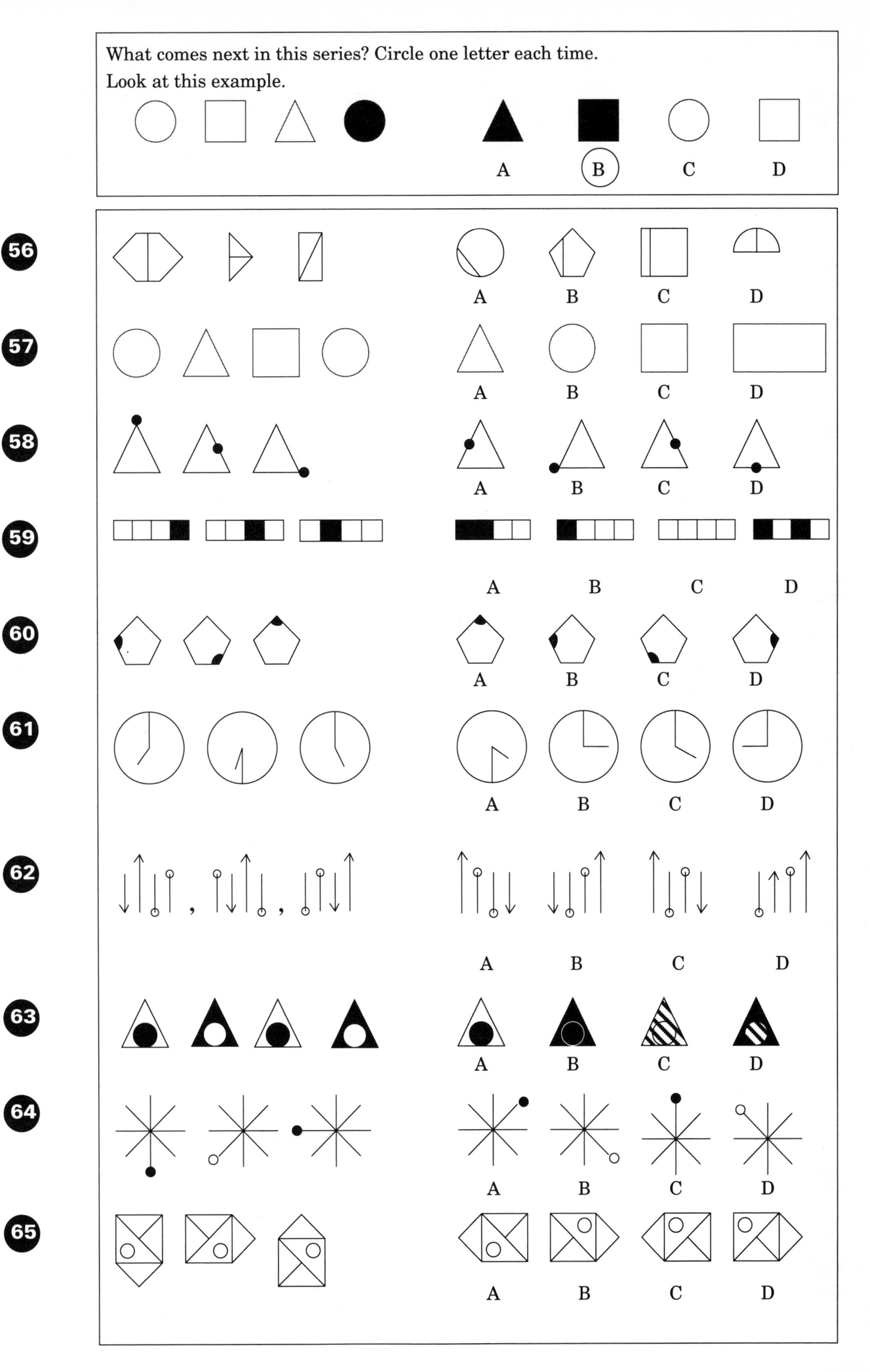
What comes next in this series? Circle one letter each time.
Look at this example.
A B C D
56
A B C D
57
A B C D
58
A B C D
59
A B C D
60
A B C D
61
A B C D
62
A B C D
63
A B C D
64
A B C D
65
A B C D

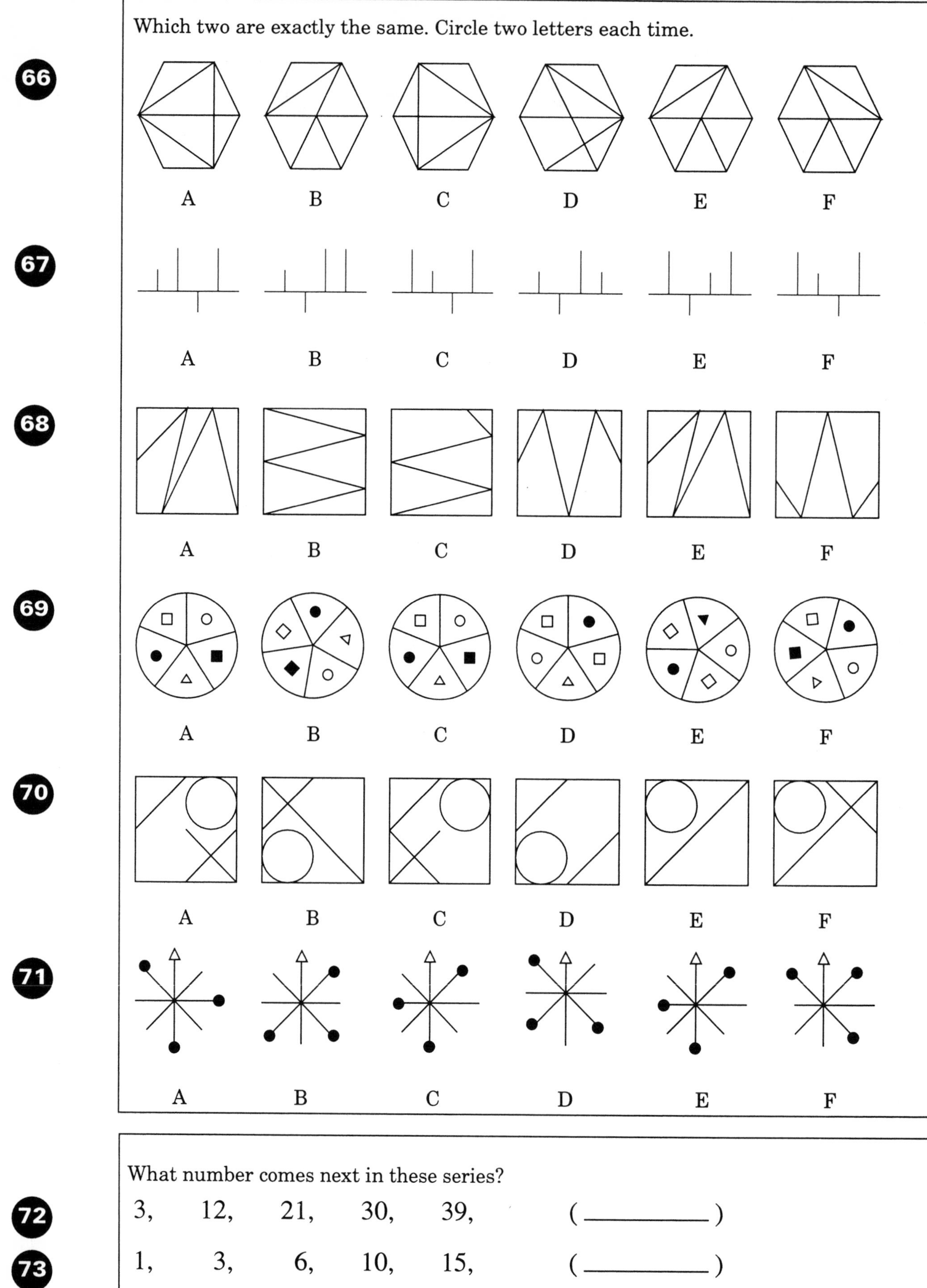

What number comes next in these series?

3, 12, 21, 30, 39, (________)

1, 3, 6, 10, 15, (________)

4, 9, 16, 25, 36, (________)

43, 37, 31, 25, 19, (________)

TEST 03

SCORE ____________

Which shape is the same but facing the opposite direction?

Look at this example:

A B C (D)

1 A B C D

2 A B C D

3 A B C D

4 A B C D

5 A B C D

6 A B C D

7 A B C D

8 A B C D

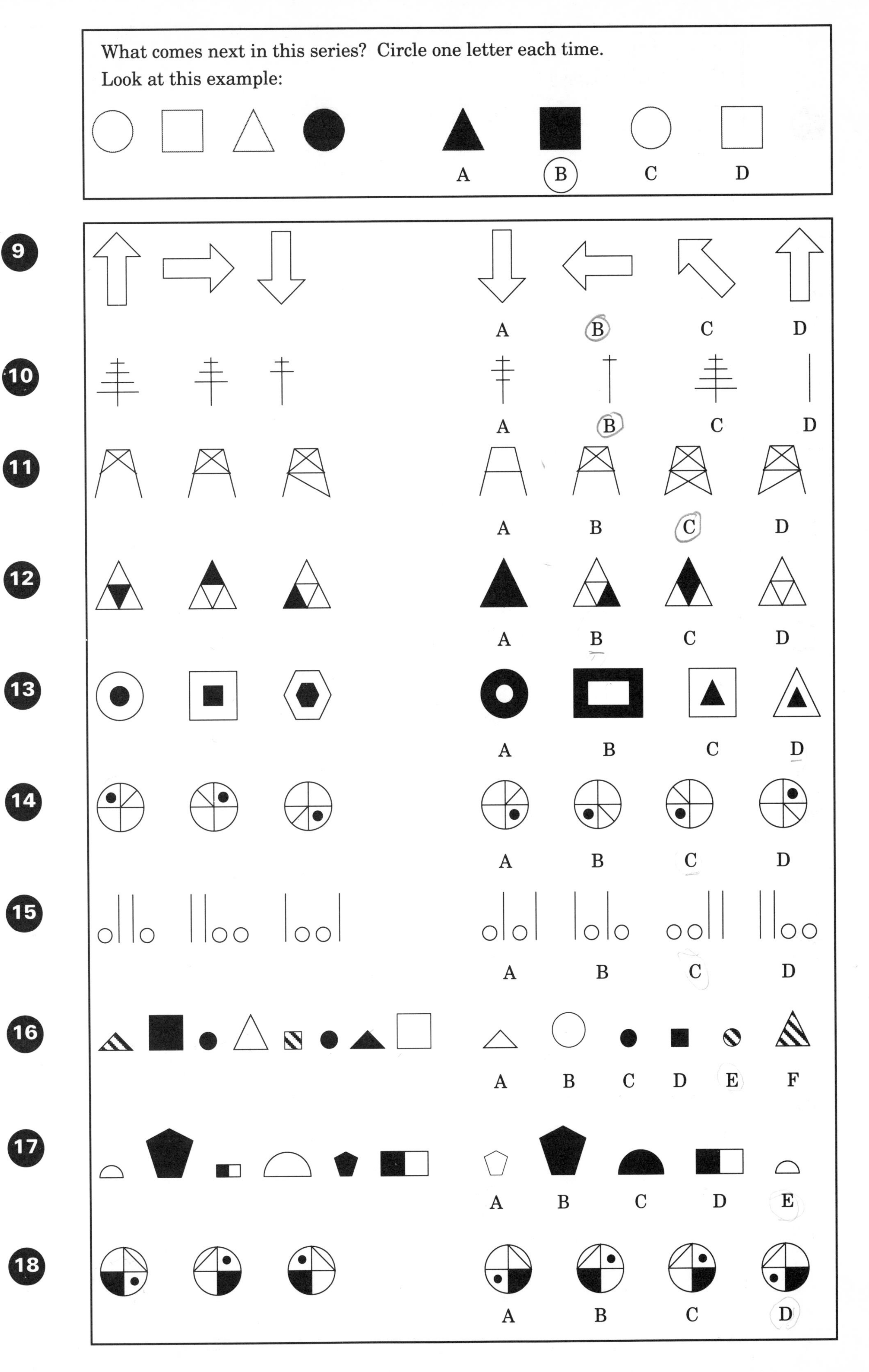
What comes next in this series? Circle one letter each time.
Look at this example:
A B C D
9
A B C D
10
A B C D
11
A B C D
12
A B C D
13
A B C D
14
A B C D
15
A B C D
16
A B C D E F
17
A B C D E
18
A B C D

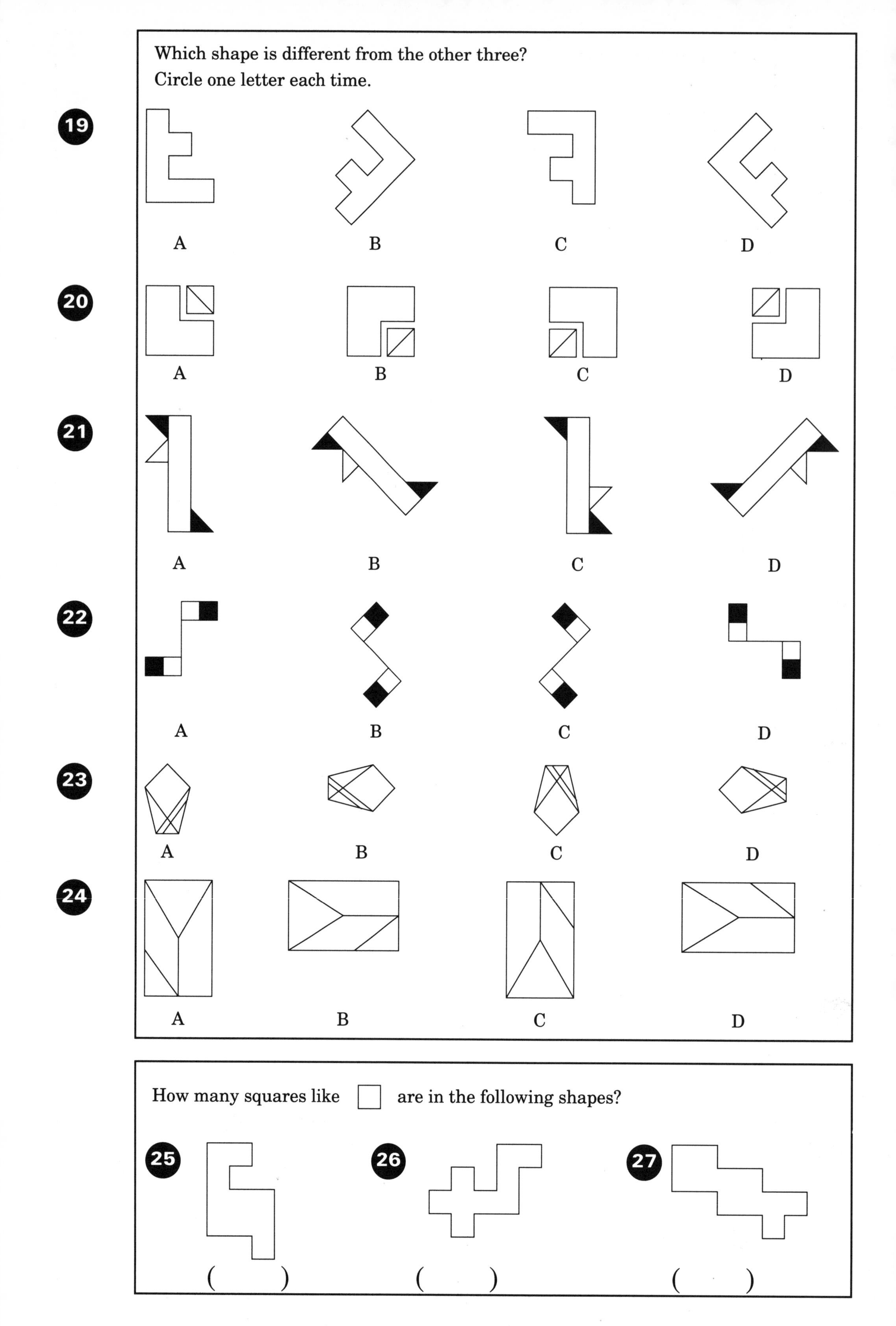
Which shape is different from the other three?
Circle one letter each time.
19
A
B
C
D
20
A
B
C
D
21
A
B
C
D
22
A
B
C
D
23
A
B
C
D
24
A
B
C
D
How many squares like
are in the following shapes?
25
( )
26
( )
27
( )

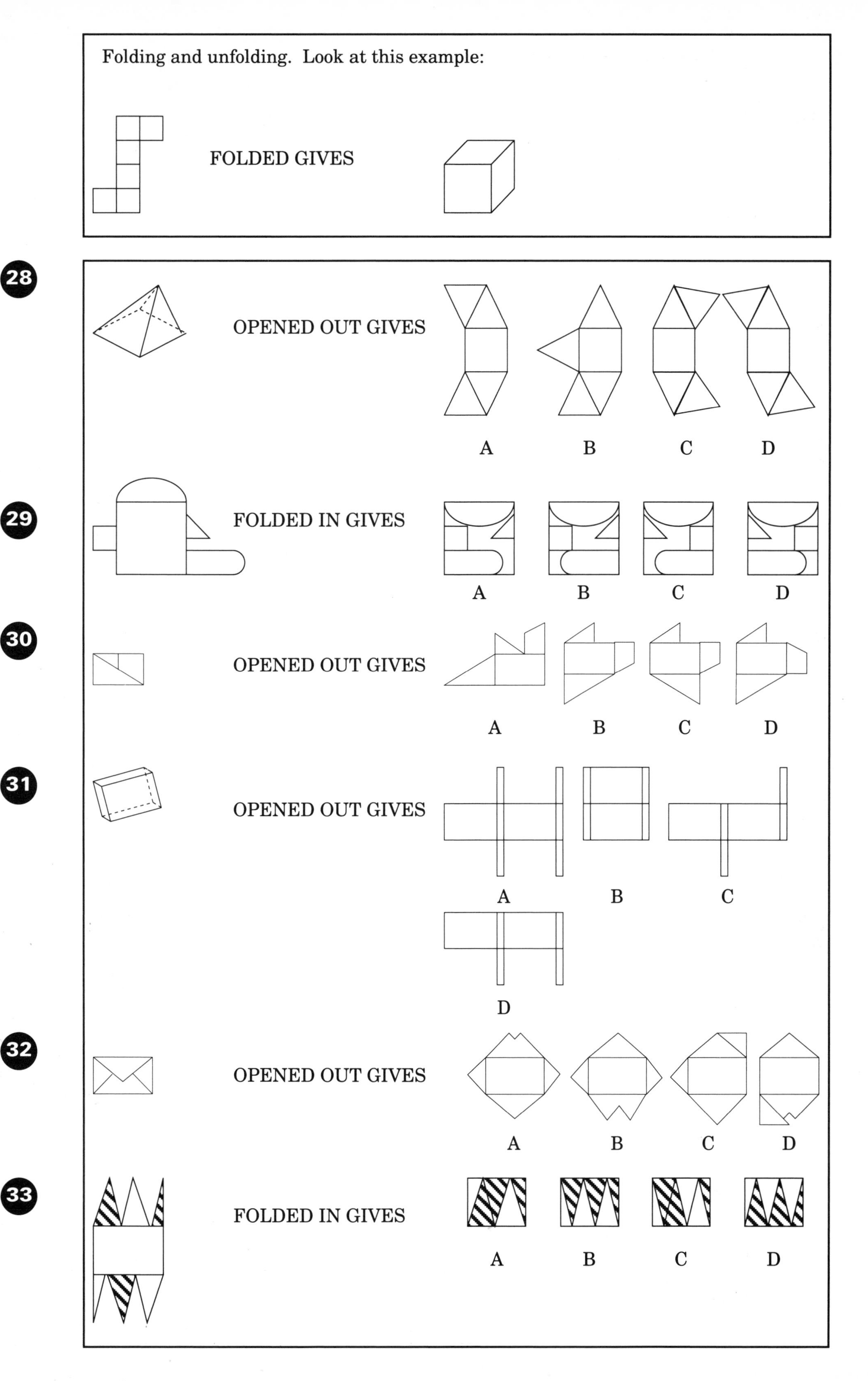
Folding and unfolding. Look at this example:
FOLDED GIVES
28
OPENED OUT GIVES
A
B
C
D
29
FOLDED IN GIVES
A
B
C
D
30
OPENED OUT GIVES
A
B
C
D
31
OPENED OUT GIVES
A
B
C
D
32
OPENED OUT GIVES
A
B
C
D
33
FOLDED IN GIVES
A
B
C
D

Which is the odd one out in this group of shapes? Circle one letter each time.
Look at this example:

A B C (D)

34 A B C D E

35 A B C D E

36 A B C D E

37 A B C D E

38 A B C D E

39 A B C D E

40 A B C D E

41 A B C D E

42 A B C D E

43 A B C D E

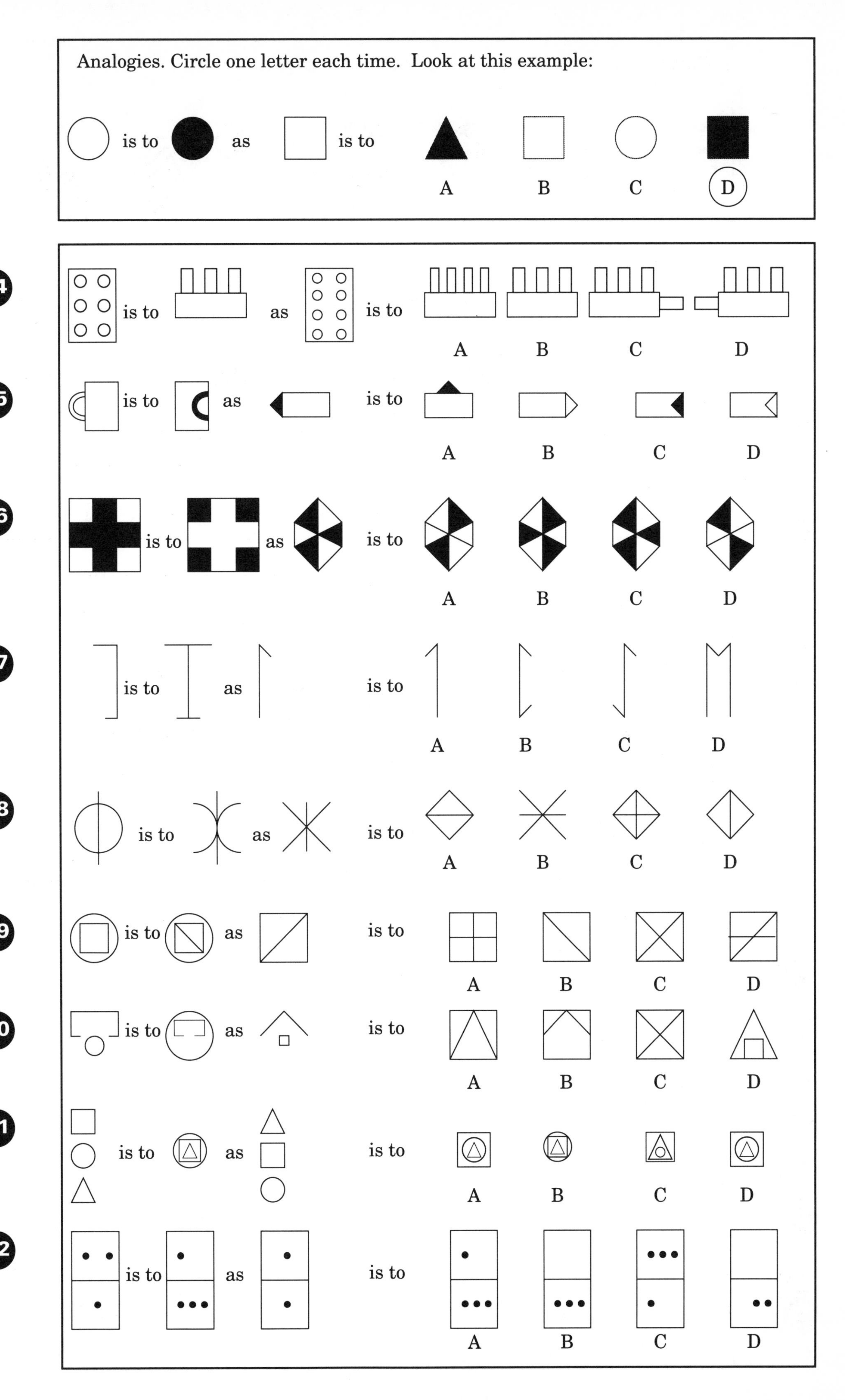
Analogies. Circle one letter each time. Look at this example:
is to
as
is to
A
B
C
D
44
is to
as
is to
A
B
C
D
45
is to
as
is to
A
B
C
D
46
is to
as
is to
A
B
C
D
47
is to
as
is to
A
B
C
D
48
is to
as
is to
A
B
C
D
49
is to
as
is to
A
B
C
D
50
is to
as
is to
A
B
C
D
51
is to
as
is to
A
B
C
D
52
is to
as
is to
A
B
C
D

What fraction is shaded each time? Circle one answer.

53

$\frac{2}{3}$ $\frac{3}{4}$ $\frac{5}{8}$ $\frac{1}{2}$

54

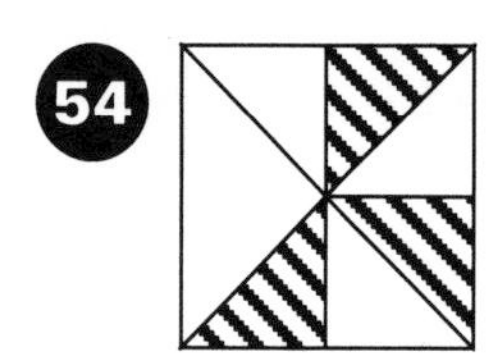

$\frac{1}{4}$ $\frac{3}{8}$ $\frac{1}{3}$ $\frac{1}{2}$

55

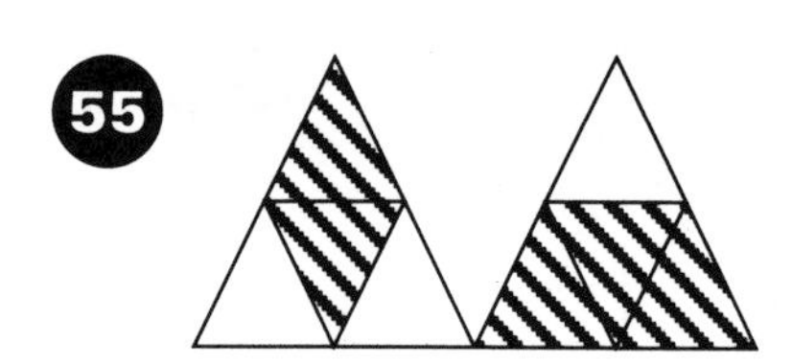

$\frac{5}{8}$ $\frac{3}{4}$ $\frac{2}{3}$ $\frac{5}{6}$

56

$\frac{1}{5}$ $\frac{1}{3}$ $\frac{3}{10}$ $\frac{1}{4}$

57

$\frac{3}{12}$ $\frac{1}{6}$ $\frac{1}{3}$ $\frac{3}{8}$

58

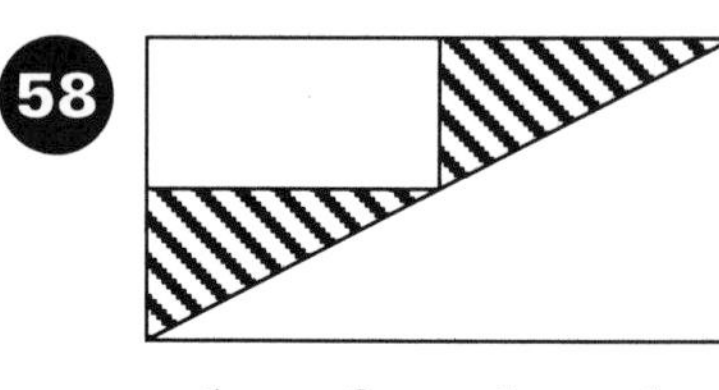

$\frac{1}{8}$ $\frac{3}{8}$ $\frac{1}{4}$ $\frac{1}{5}$

Complete this mathematical table.

59 **60** **61** **62** **63** **64** **65** **66** **67**

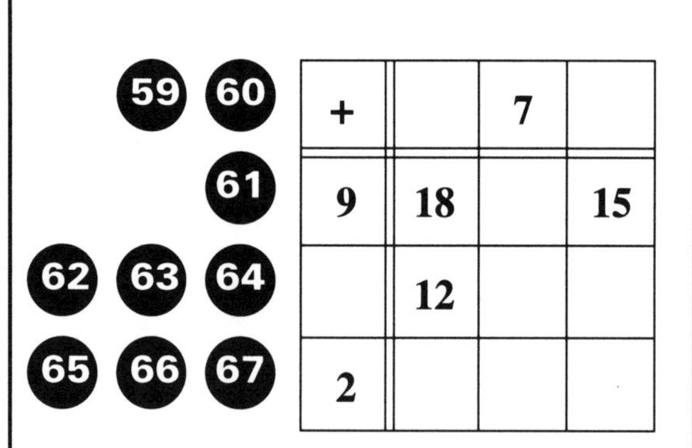

+		7	
9	18		15
	12		
2			

Supply the missing numbers.

68 **69** **70** **71**

$$\begin{array}{r} 3\ 5\ \square \\ +\ 2\ \square\ 7 \\ \square\ 6\ 3 \\ \hline \square\ 5\ 2\ 4 \end{array}$$

Give the next number in each series.

72 1, 4, 9, 16, 25, (________)

73 1, 2, 4, 8, 16, (________)

74 3, 7, 12, 16, 21, (________)

75 40, 33, 26, 19, 12, (________)

TEST 04

SCORE ___________

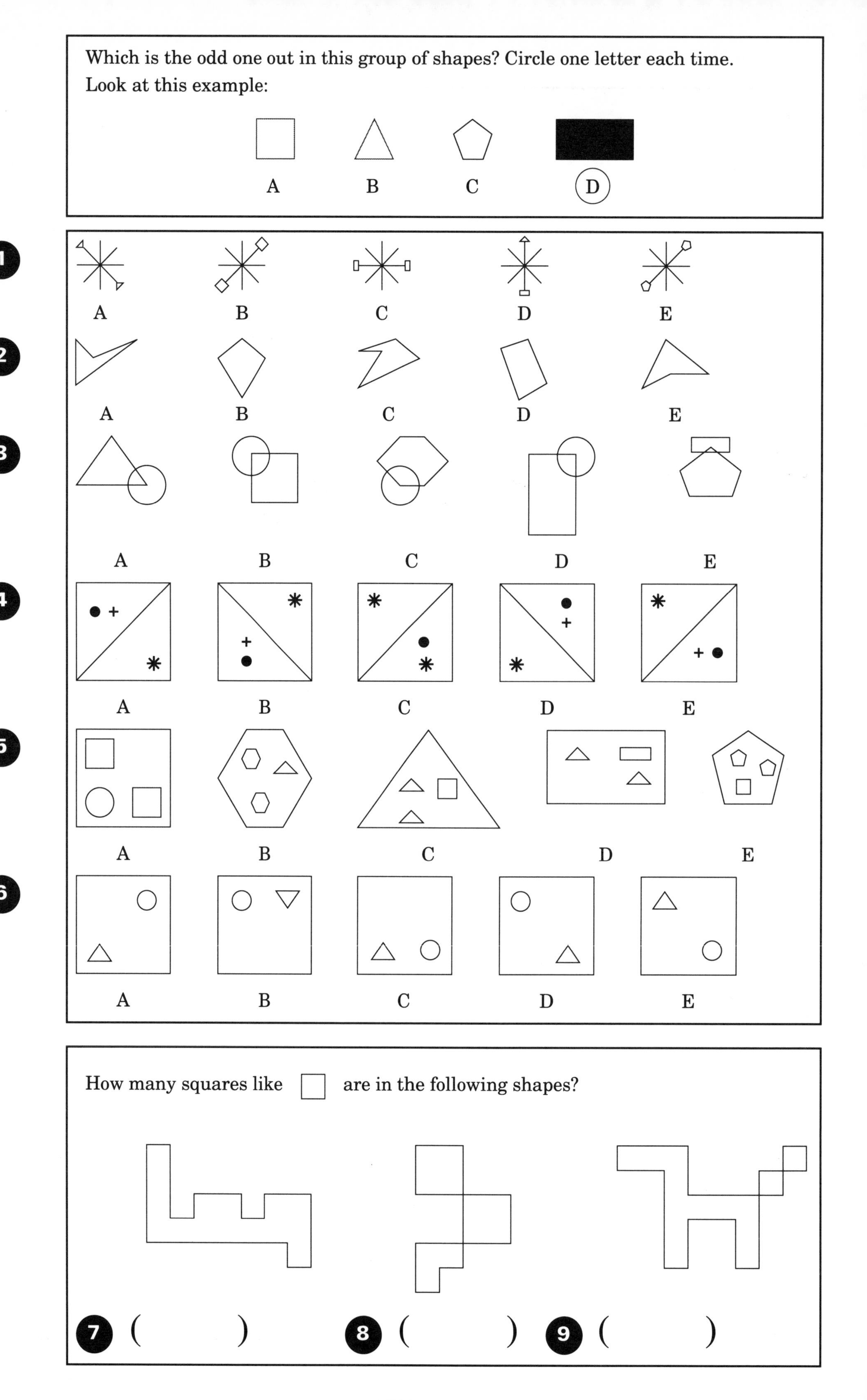
Which is the odd one out in this group of shapes? Circle one letter each time.
Look at this example:
A B C D
1
A B C D E
2
A B C D E
3
A B C D E
4
A B C D E
5
A B C D E
6
A B C D E
How many squares like are in the following shapes?
7 ( )
8 ( )
9 ( )

Which shape is the same but facing the opposite direction?

Look at this example:

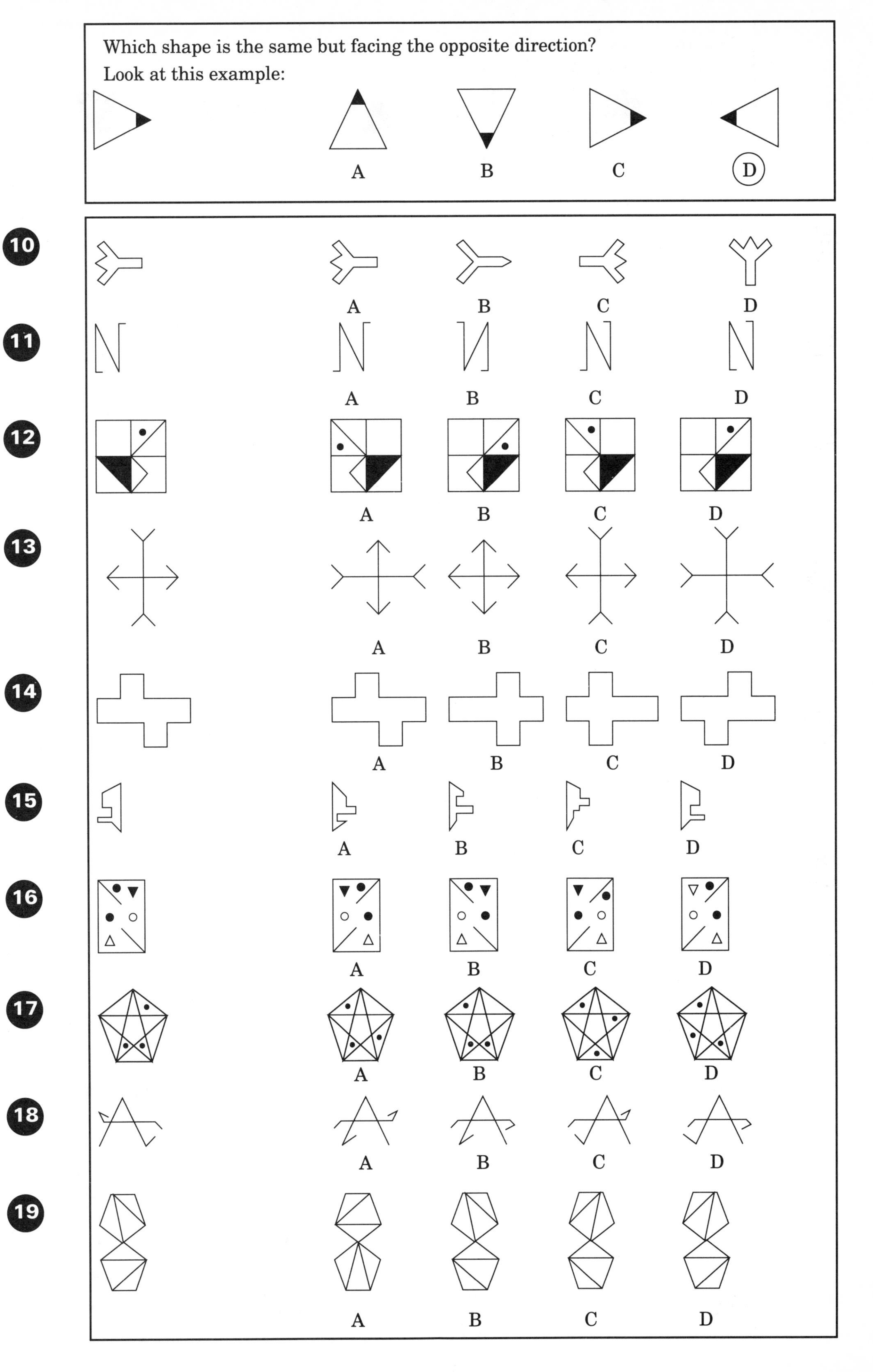

Analogies. Circle one letter each time. Look at this example:

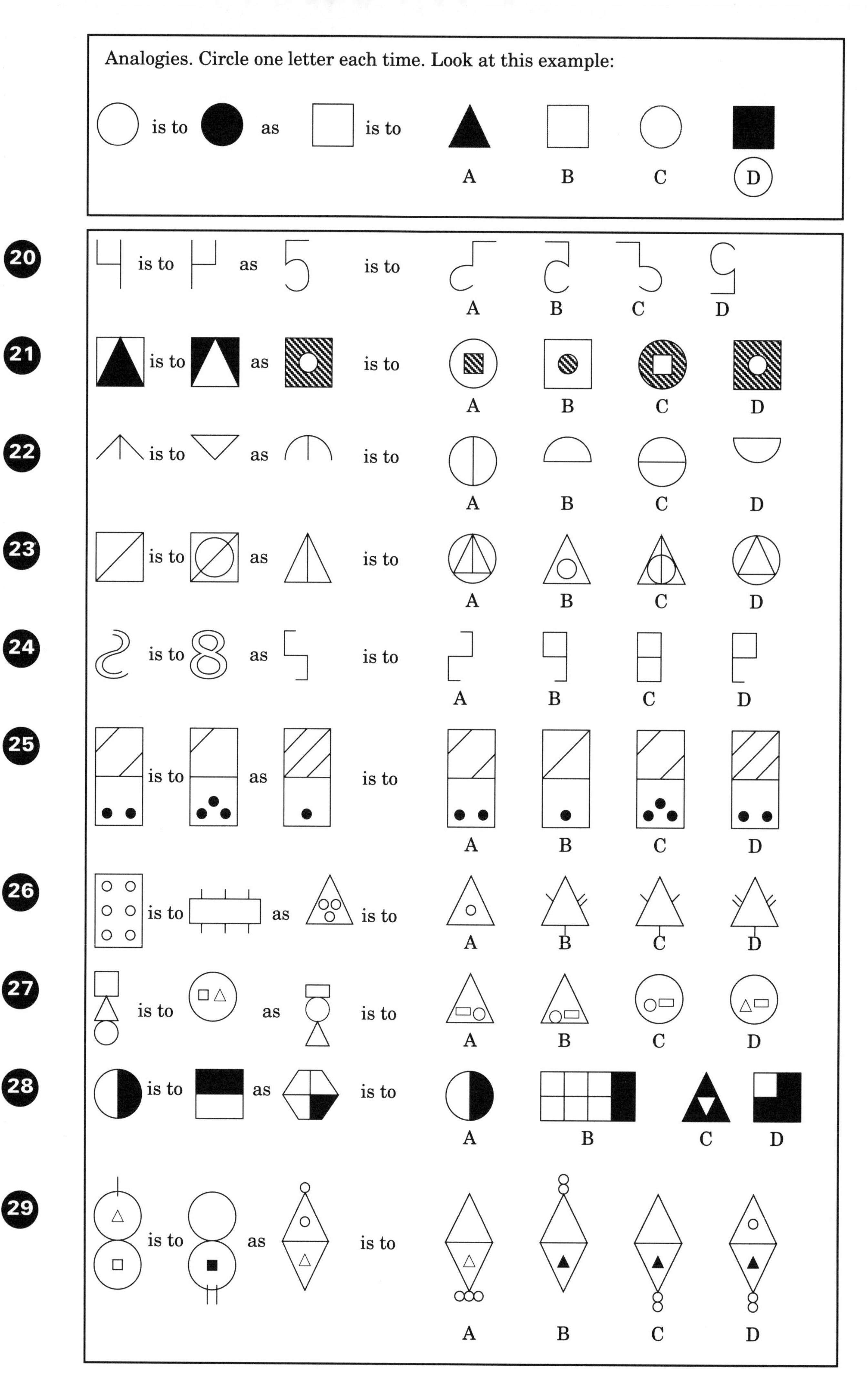

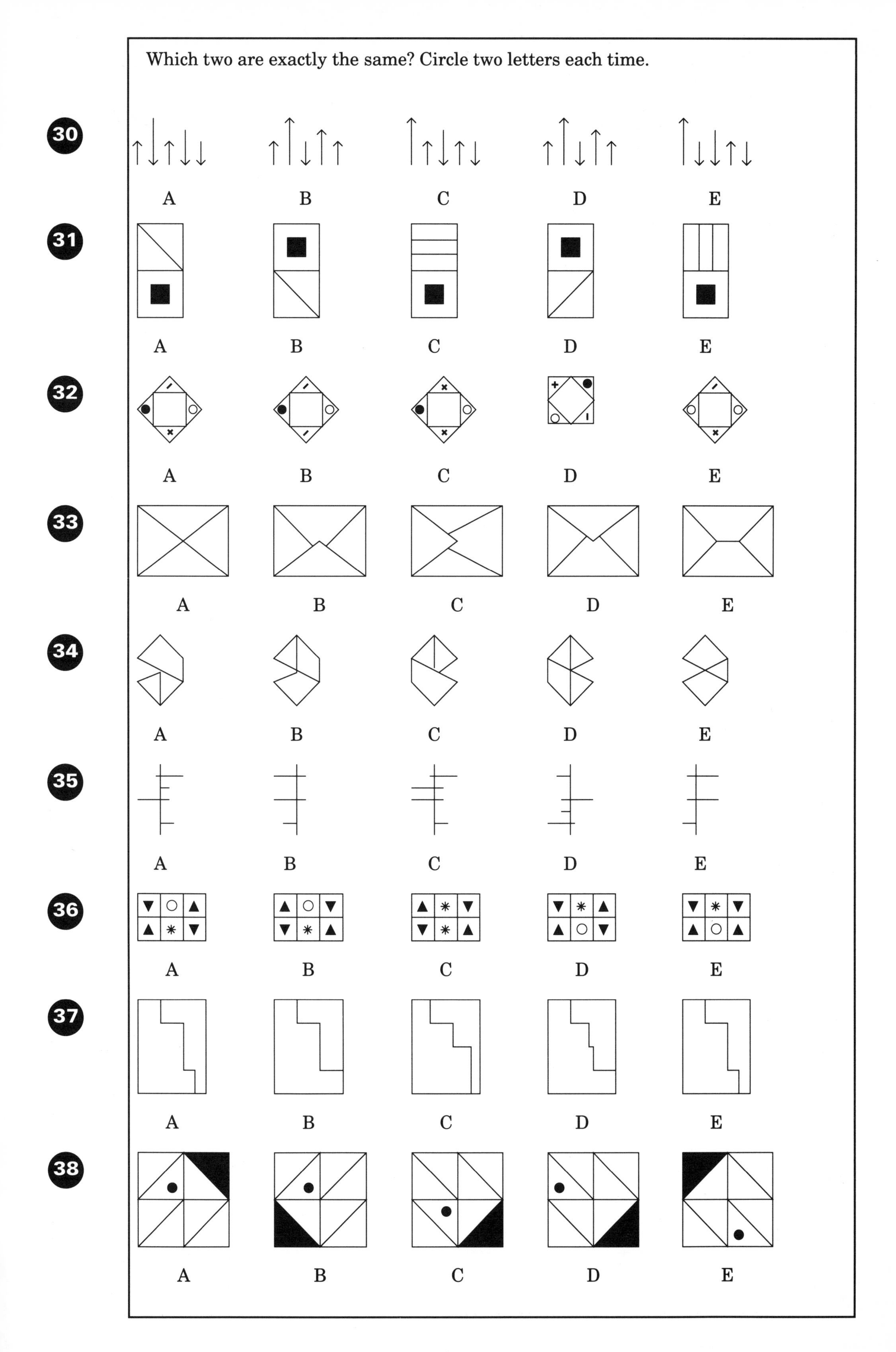
Which two are exactly the same? Circle two letters each time.
30
A
B
C
D
E
31
A
B
C
D
E
32
A
B
C
D
E
33
A
B
C
D
E
34
A
B
C
D
E
35
A
B
C
D
E
36
A
B
C
D
E
37
A
B
C
D
E
38
A
B
C
D
E

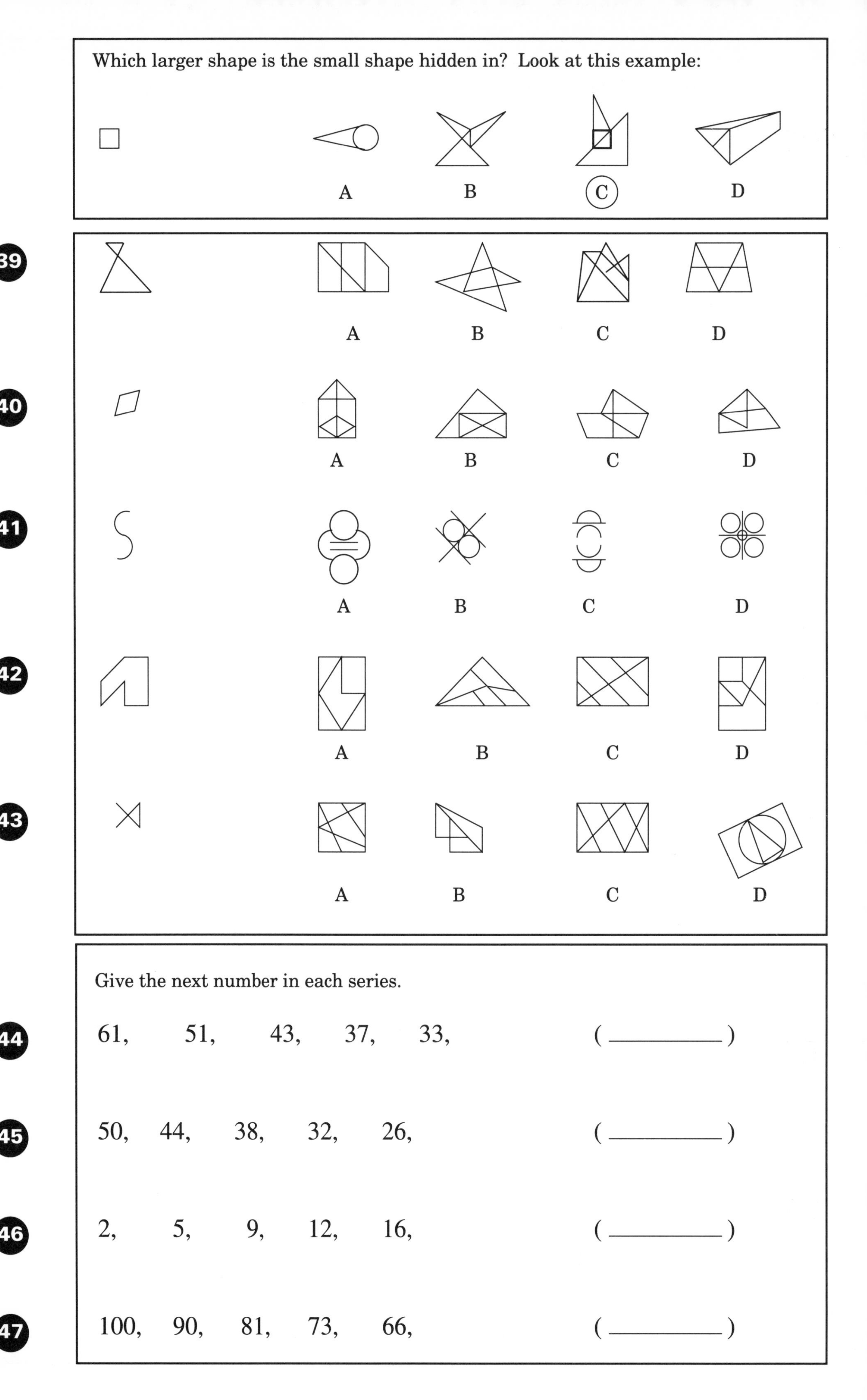
Which larger shape is the small shape hidden in? Look at this example:
A
B
C
D
39
40
41
42
43
Give the next number in each series.
44
61, 51, 43, 37, 33, ( )
45
50, 44, 38, 32, 26, ( )
46
2, 5, 9, 12, 16, ( )
47
100, 90, 81, 73, 66, ( )

Without turning the pieces over choose which piece completes the white jig-saw pieces. Circle one letter each time.

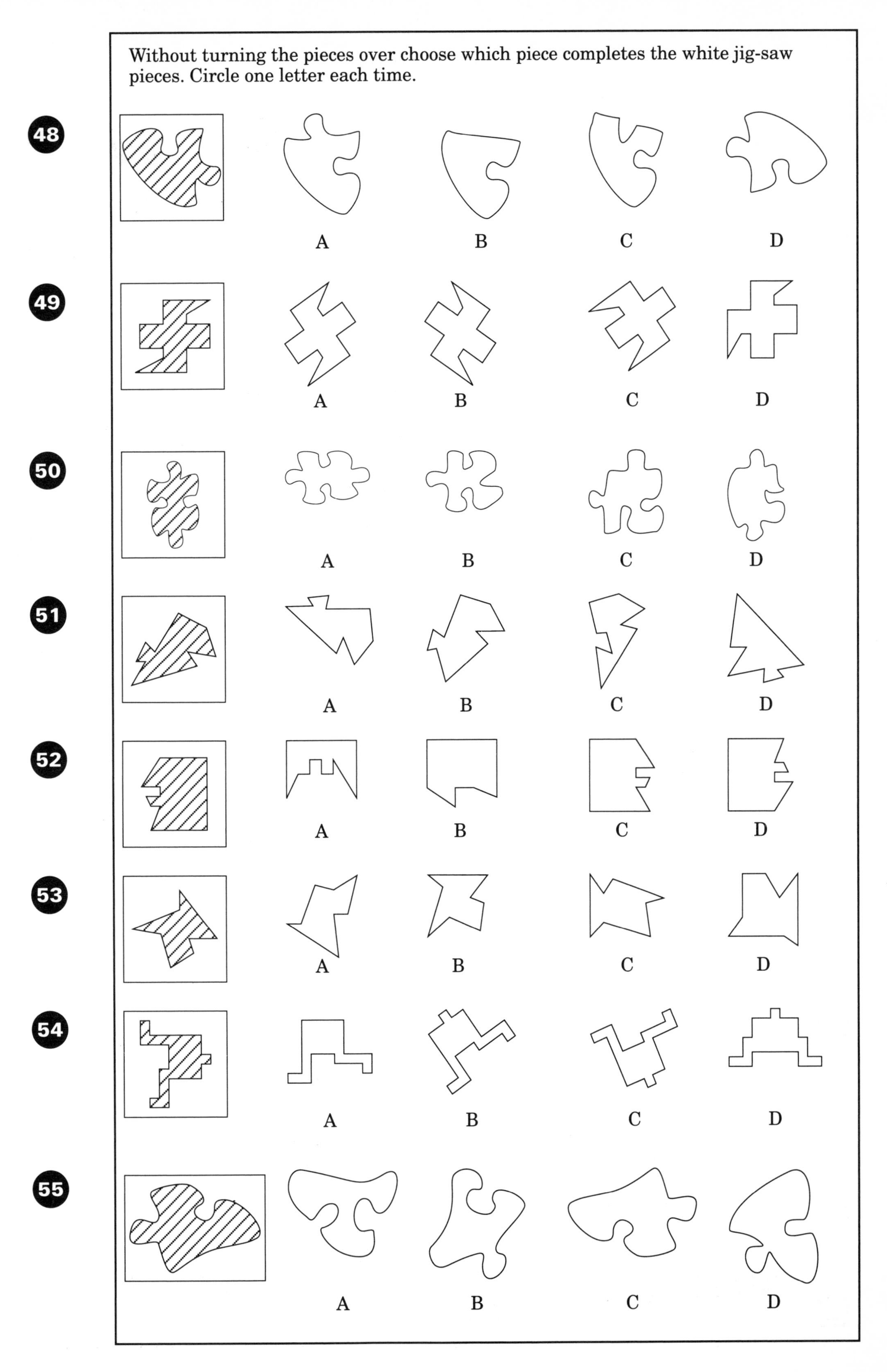

What fraction is shaded each time? Circle one answer.

56

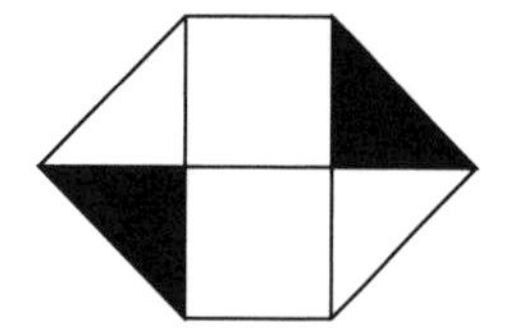

$\frac{5}{8}$ $\frac{1}{3}$ $\frac{2}{4}$ $\frac{1}{4}$

57

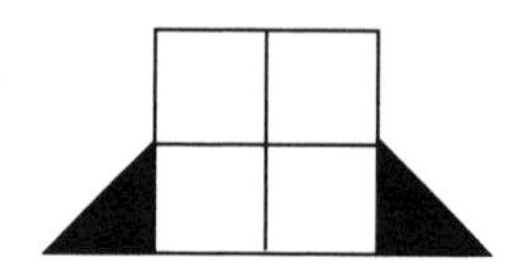

$\frac{1}{3}$ $\frac{1}{4}$ $\frac{1}{5}$ $\frac{1}{8}$

58

$\frac{4}{9}$ $\frac{1}{3}$ $\frac{1}{8}$ $\frac{5}{8}$

59

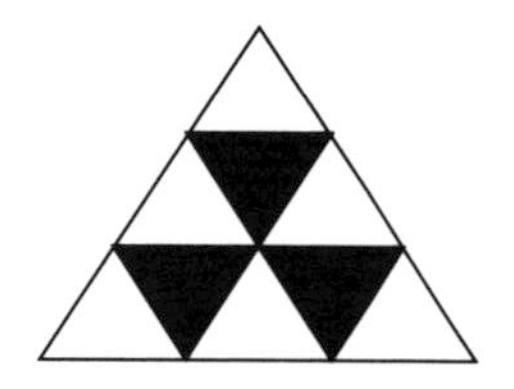

$\frac{4}{9}$ $\frac{1}{3}$ $\frac{3}{4}$ $\frac{5}{8}$

60

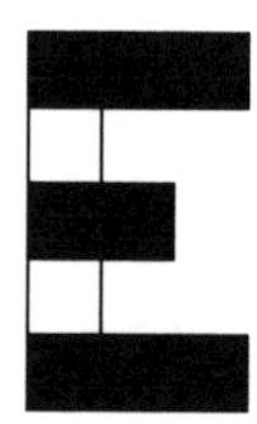

$\frac{7}{10}$ $\frac{4}{5}$ $\frac{6}{9}$ $\frac{5}{6}$

61

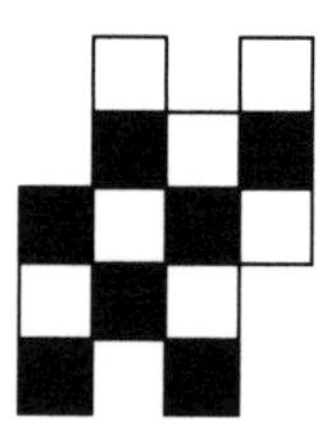

$\frac{9}{12}$ $\frac{1}{2}$ $\frac{8}{14}$ $\frac{5}{7}$

62

$\frac{4}{8}$ $\frac{2}{3}$ $\frac{1}{3}$ $\frac{5}{6}$

63

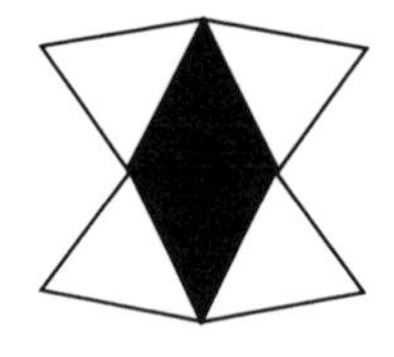

$\frac{2}{3}$ $\frac{1}{6}$ $\frac{1}{3}$ $\frac{3}{6}$

Subtract the numbers in the left hand column from those in the top row.

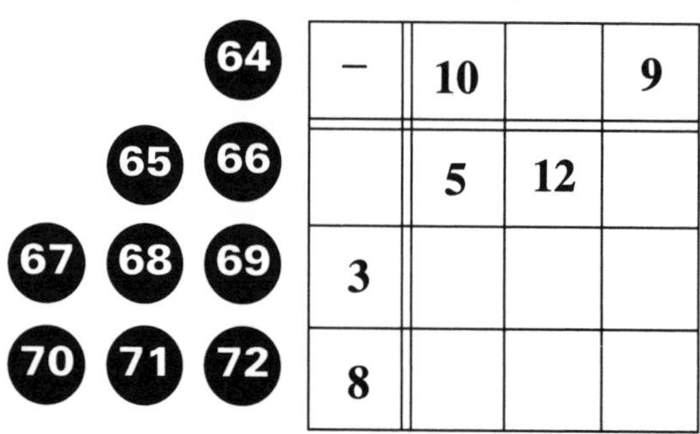

−	10		9
	5	12	
3			
8			

Supply the missing numbers.

5 □ 2

+ 4 3 6

□ 6 □

1 5 2 2

TEST 05

SCORE ____________

Which shape is the same but facing the opposite direction?
Circle one letter each time. Look at this example.

A B C (D)

1
A B C D

2
A B C D

3
A B C D

4
A B C D

5
A B C D

6
A B C D

7
A B C D

8
A B C D

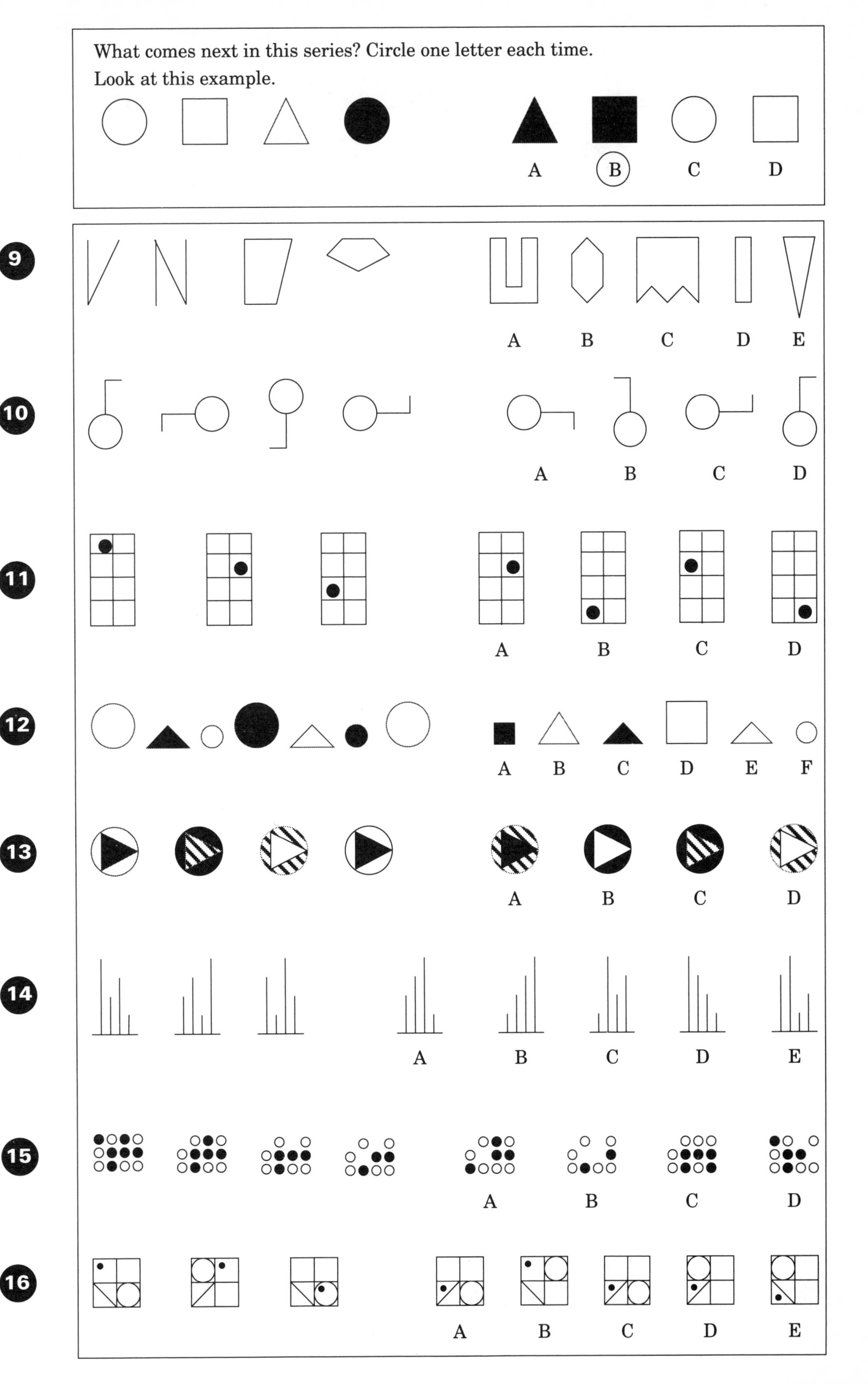
What comes next in this series? Circle one letter each time.
Look at this example.
A B C D
9
A B C D E
10
A B C D
11
A B C D
12
A B C D E F
13
A B C D
14
A B C D E
15
A B C D
16
A B C D E

What fraction is shaded each time? Circle one answer.

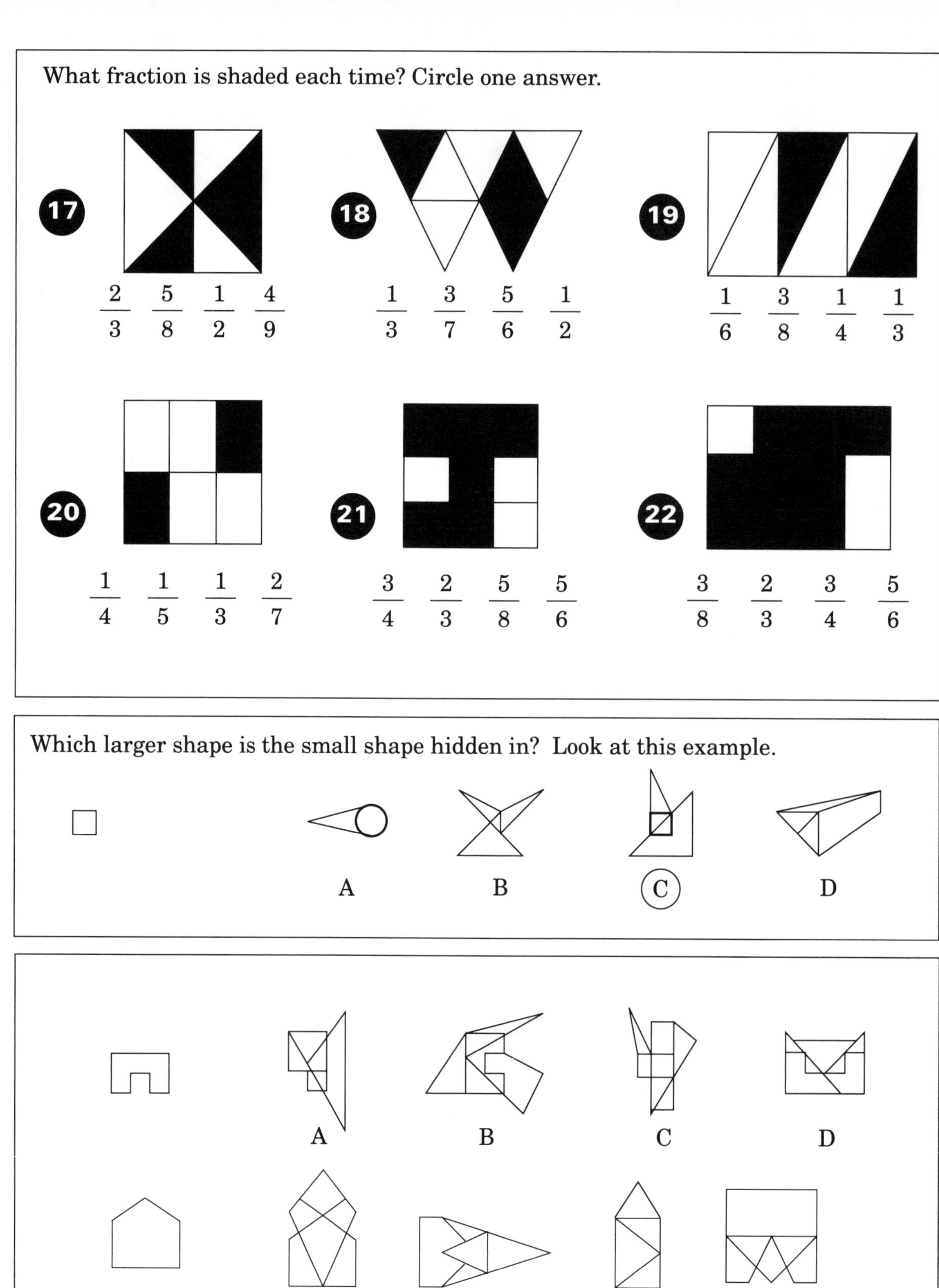

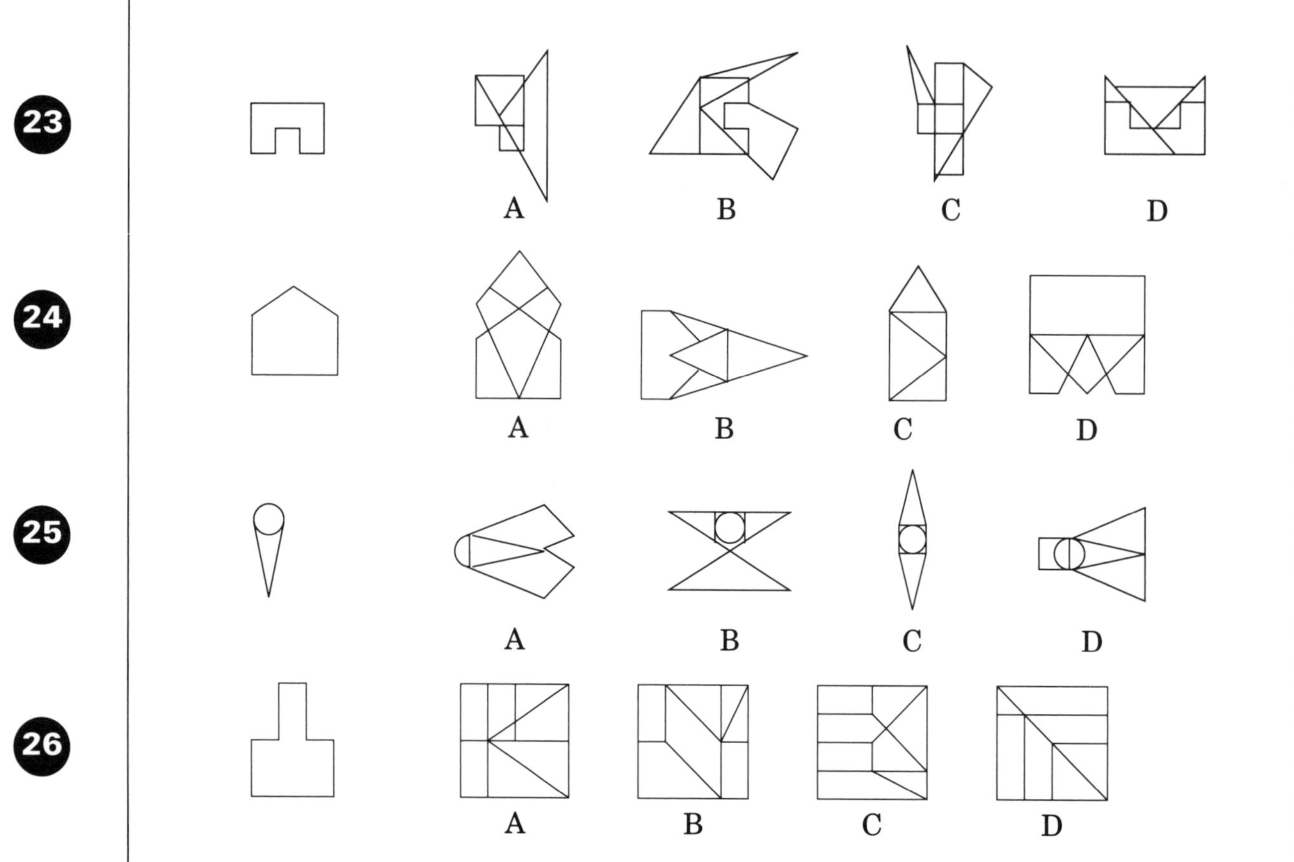

In these questions the two shapes are either added together or subtracted from each other. The shapes do not turn. Circle one answer. Look at this example:

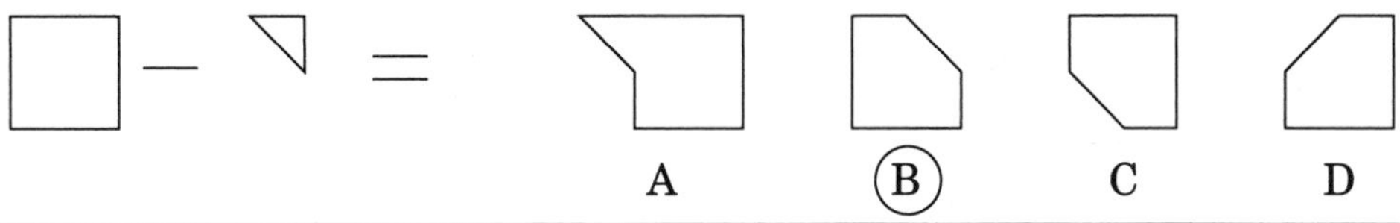

27 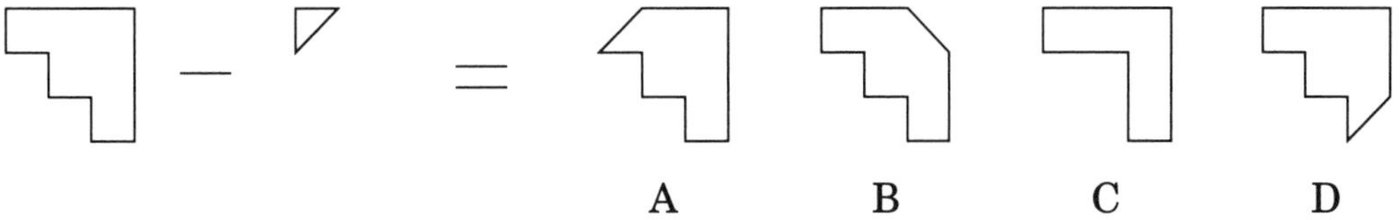

28 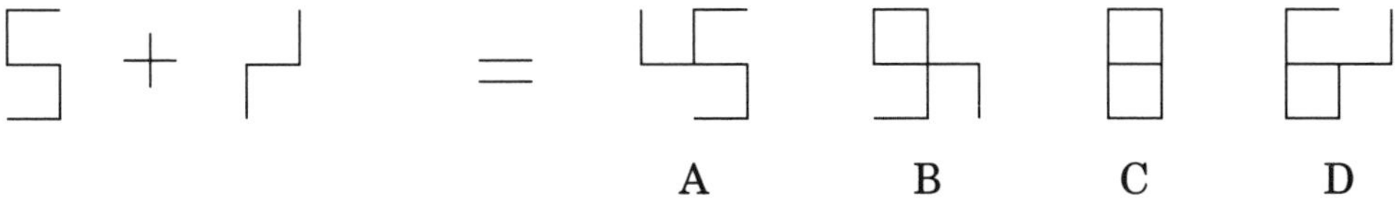

29 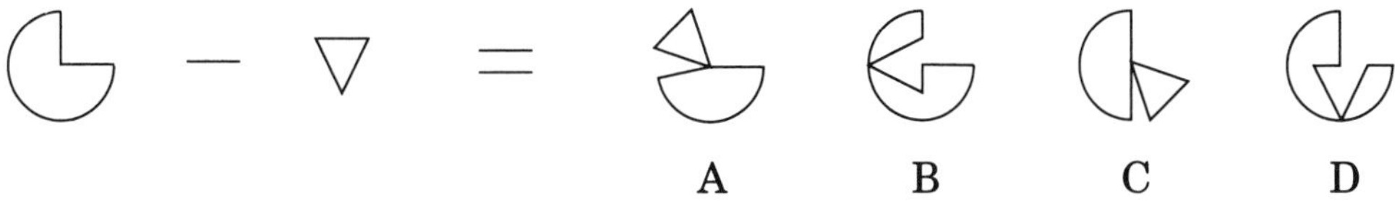

30 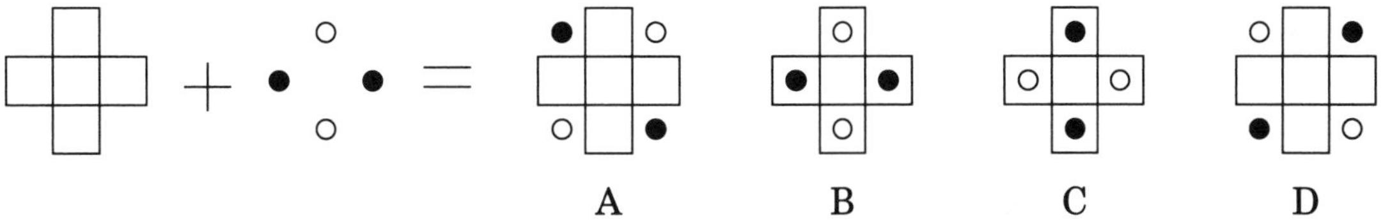

31 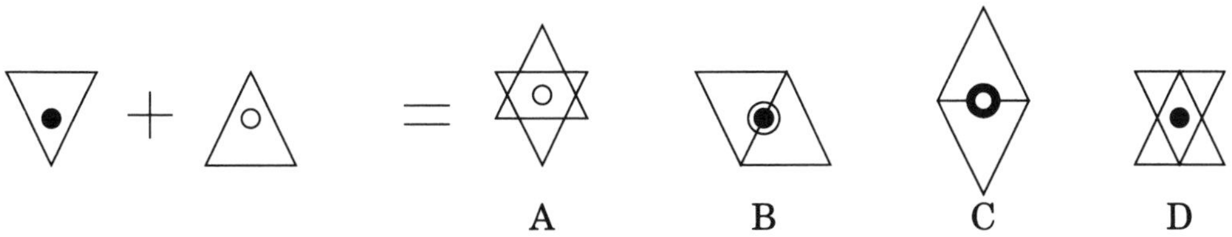

32 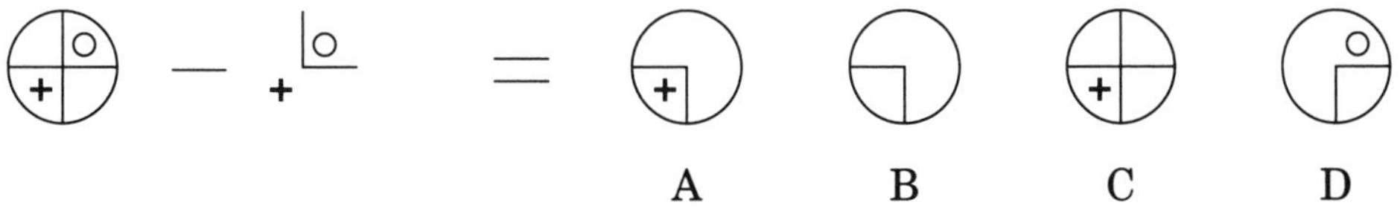

33 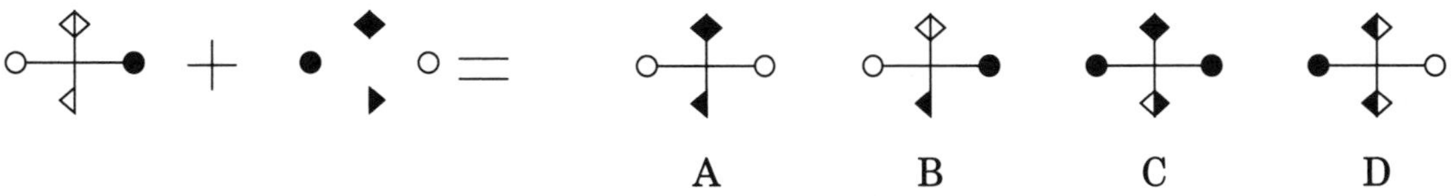

Which number does not belong in the series? Circle your answer.

34 15, 20, 25, 30, 36, 40, 45.

35 7, 14, 21, 28, 35, 42, 48.

36 4, 7, 10, 14, 16, 19, 22.

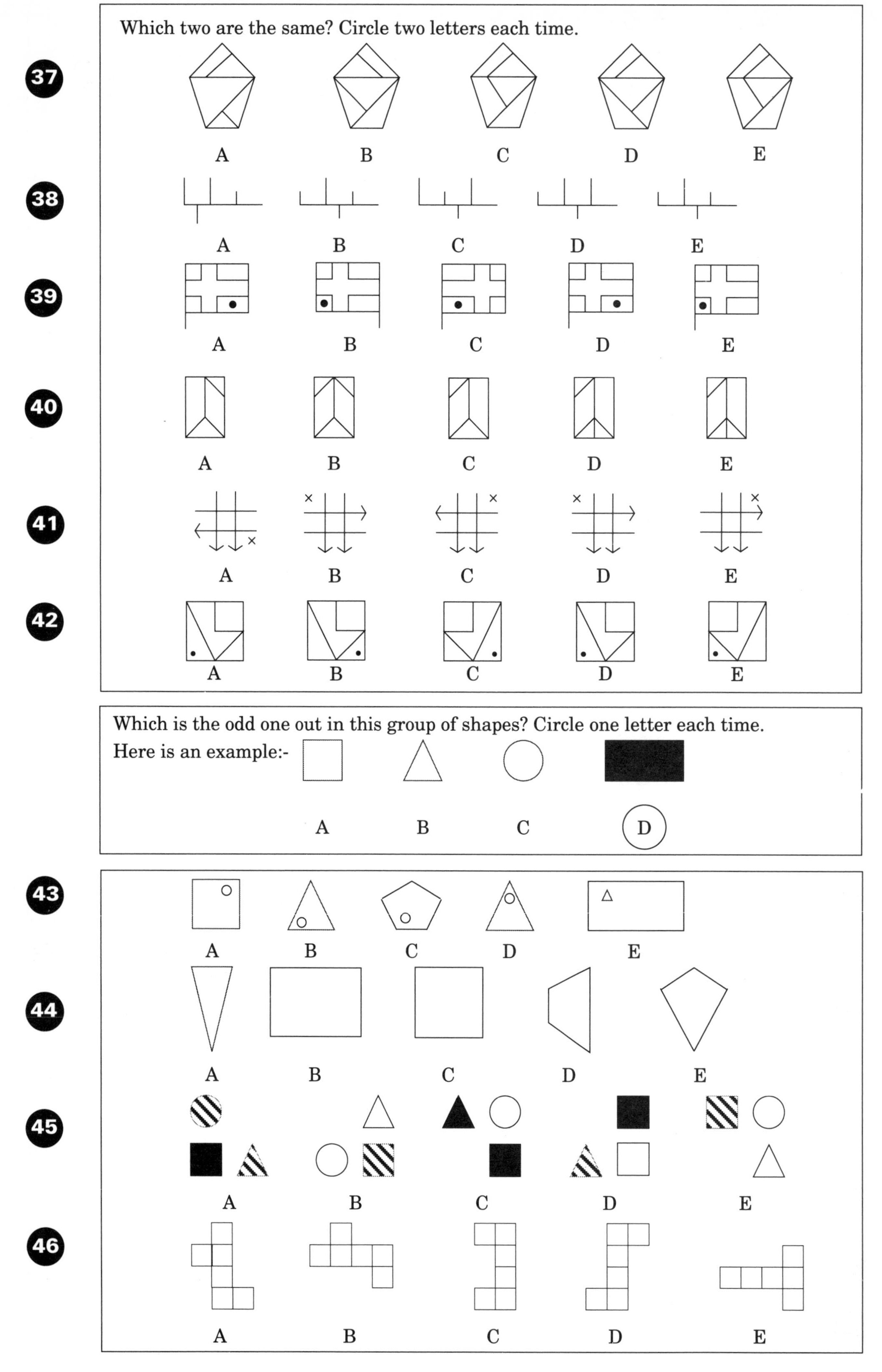
Which two are the same? Circle two letters each time.
37
A B C D E
38
A B C D E
39
A B C D E
40
A B C D E
41
A B C D E
42
A B C D E
Which is the odd one out in this group of shapes? Circle one letter each time.
Here is an example:-
A B C D
43
A B C D E
44
A B C D E
45
A B C D E
46
A B C D E

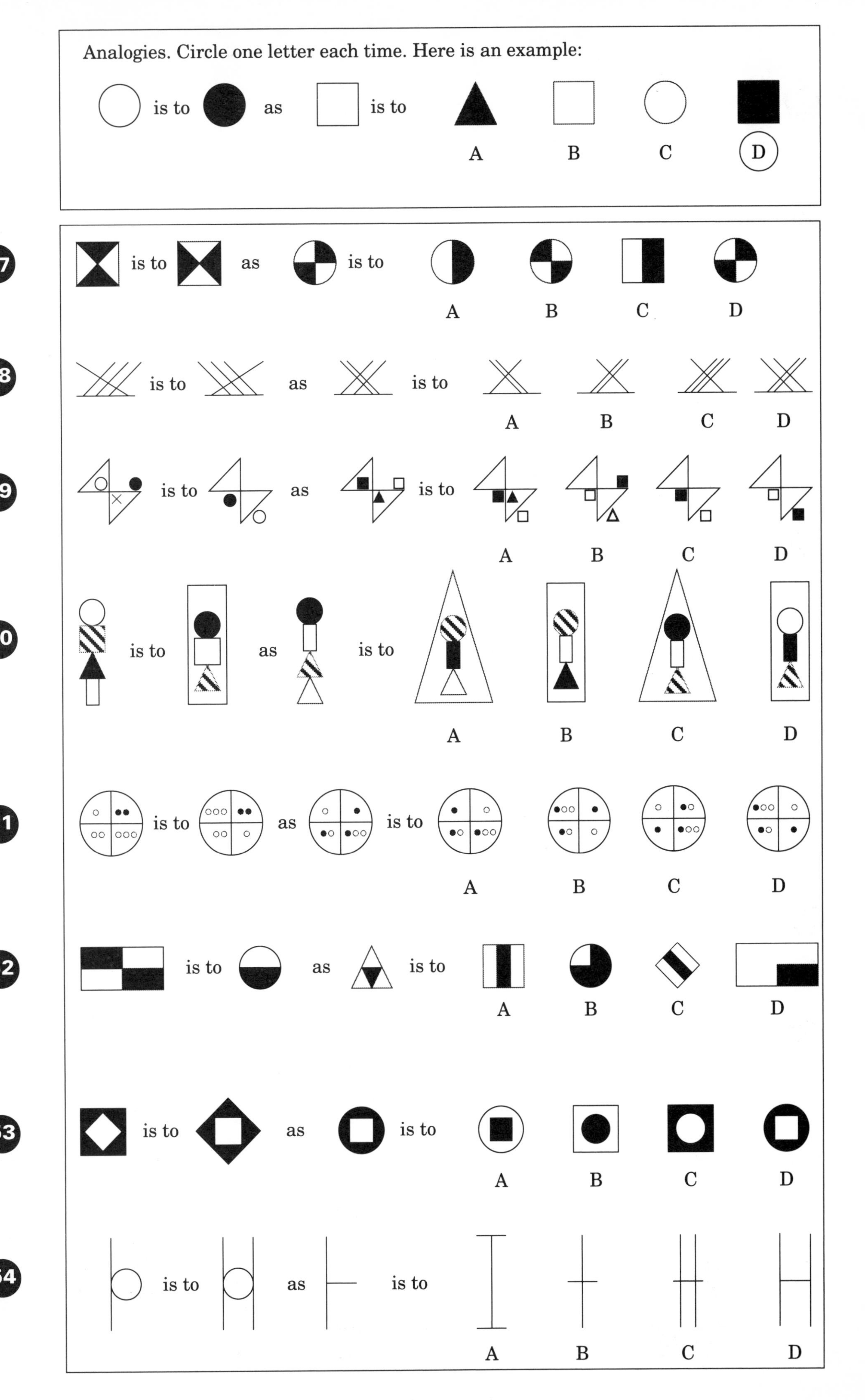
Analogies. Circle one letter each time. Here is an example:
is to
as
is to
A
B
C
D
47
is to
as
is to
A
B
C
D
48
is to
as
is to
A
B
C
D
49
is to
as
is to
A
B
C
D
50
is to
as
is to
A
B
C
D
51
is to
as
is to
A
B
C
D
52
is to
as
is to
A
B
C
D
53
is to
as
is to
A
B
C
D
54
is to
as
is to
A
B
C
D

Which shape is different from the other four? Circle one letter each time.

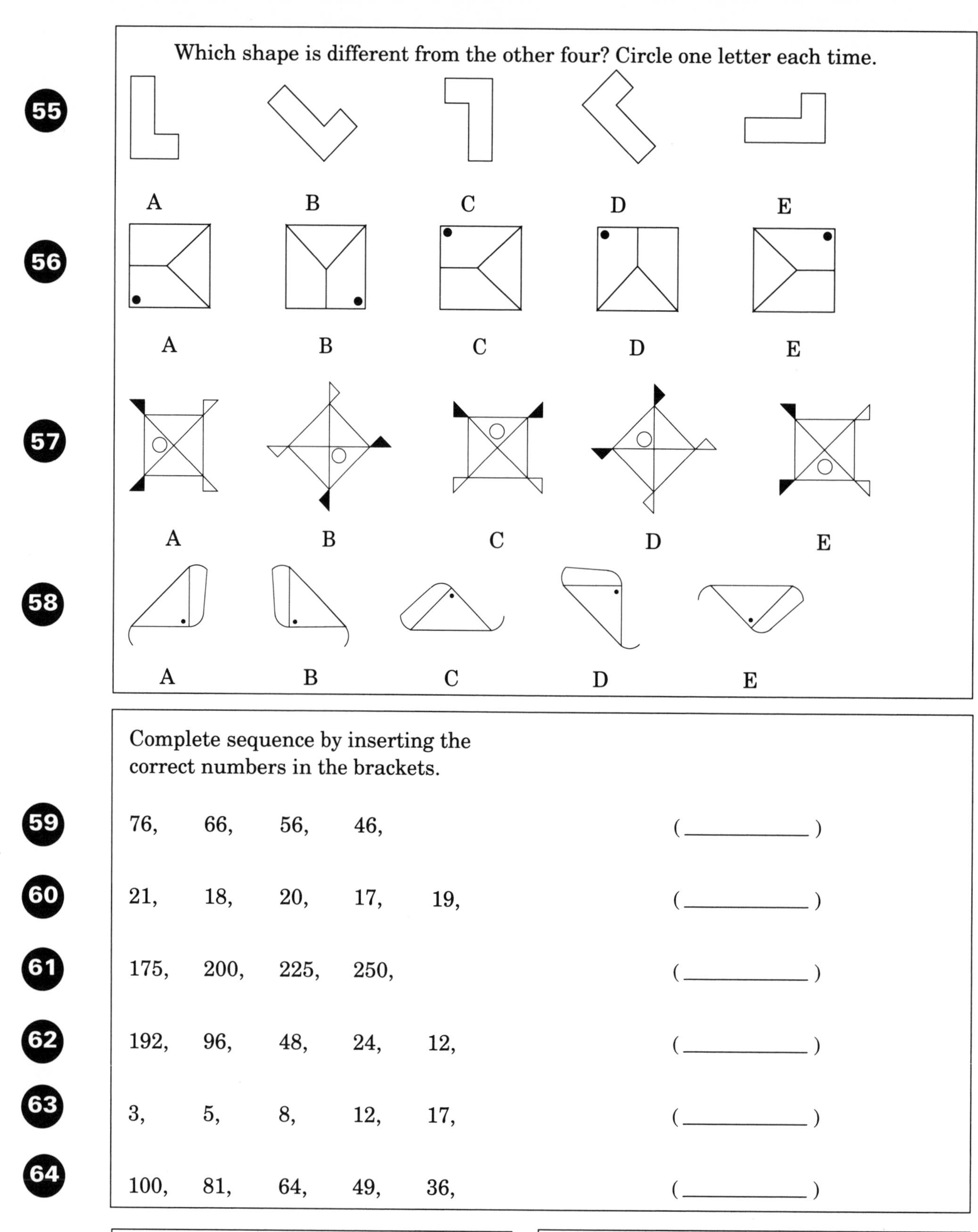

55 A B C D E

56 A B C D E

57 A B C D E

58 A B C D E

Complete sequence by inserting the correct numbers in the brackets.

59 76, 66, 56, 46, (__________)

60 21, 18, 20, 17, 19, (__________)

61 175, 200, 225, 250, (__________)

62 192, 96, 48, 24, 12, (__________)

63 3, 5, 8, 12, 17, (__________)

64 100, 81, 64, 49, 36, (__________)

Complete this mathematical table.

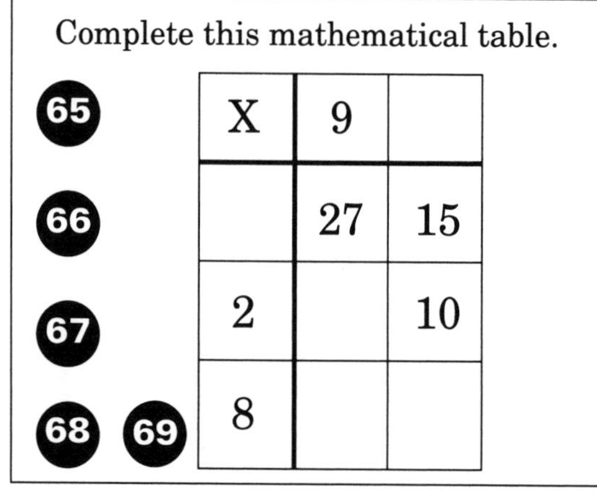

65 **66** **67** **68** **69**

X	9	
	27	15
2		10
8		

Supply the missing numbers.

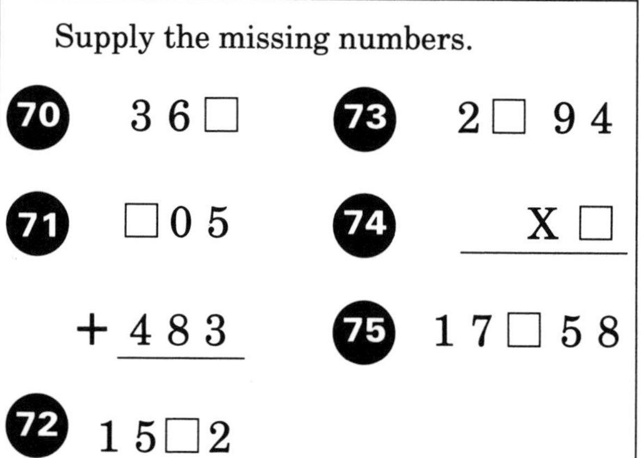

70 3 6 □

71 □ 0 5

+ 4 8 3

72 1 5 □ 2

73 2 □ 9 4

74 X □

75 1 7 □ 5 8

ANSWER TO TEST 01

1. C and E
2. B and D
3. A and D
4. A and E
5. B and D
6. 2/3
7. 3/8
8. 1/2
9. 4/7
10. 5/9
11. 3/8
12. E
13. E
14. B
15. C
16. D
17. D
18. F
19. D
20. E
21. C
22. C
23. B
24. A
25. C
26. E
27. B
28. D
29. D
30. C
31. D
32. B
33. E
34 D
35. 3
36. 10
37. 5
38. 31
39. 2
40. A
41. B
42 D
43 D
44. D
45. C
46. C
47. B
48. A
49. C
50. B
51. A
52. D
53. D
54. D
55. C
56. C
57. A
58. C
59. D
60. A
61. C
62. D
63. 8
64. 9
65. 5
66. 40
67. 45
68. 21
69. 27
70. 32
71 28
72. 4
73. 8
74 4
75. 1

A child who has not previously attempted questions of this type may have difficulty with the first few tests. However, research shows that a child's ability to handle and understand these questions generally increases with practice.

ANSWERS TO TEST 02

1. C
2. B
3. D
4. C
5. B
6. D
7. B
8. D
9. C
10. D
11. A
12. B
13. 1/4
14. 2/5
15. 1/4
16. 1/3
17. 5/8
18. 3/8
19. D
20. A
21. C
22. B
23. D
24. B
25. C
26. C
27. D
28. C
29. C
30. D
31. D
32. B
33. E
34. 6
35. 17
36. 11
37. 29
38. 3
39. 20
40. 5
41. 23
42. 22
43. 4
44. 3
45. 2
46. A
47. D
48. A
49. D
50. B
51. C
52. D
53. B
54. B
55. D
56. D
57. A
58. D
59. B
60. C
61. A
62. C
63. A
64. D
65. C
66. B and E
67. C and F
68. A and E
69. A and C
70. B and F
71. C and E
72. 48
73. 21
74. 49
75. 13

ANSWERS TO TEST 03

1. C
2. C
3. C
4. D
5. D
6. D
7. B
8. C
9. B
10. B
11. C
12. B
13. D
14. B
15. C
16. E
17. E
18. D
19. D
20. C
21. D
22. C
23. C
24. D
25. 10
26. 9
27. 11
28. D
29. B
30. B
31. C
32. B
33. C
34. C
35. E
36. D
37. C
38. C
39. C
40. D
41. A
42. C
43. B
44. A
45. D
46. B
47. D
48. D
49. C
50. B
51. C
52. B
53. 1/2
54. 3/8
55. 5/8
56. 1/4
57. 1/6
58. 1/4
59. 9
60. 6
61. 16
62. 3
63. 10
64. 9
65. 11
66. 9
67. 8
68. 4
69. 0
70. 9
71. 1
72. 36
73. 32
74. 25
75. 5

ANSWERS TO TEST 04

1. D
2. C
3. E
4. C
5. D
6. B
7. 15
8. 11
9. 14
10. C
11. B
12. C
13. C
14. D
15. D
16. A
17. B
18. C
19. C
20. B
21. B
22. D
23. C
24. C
25. A
26. C
27. A
28. B
29. C
30. B and D
31. A and B
32. A and D
33. B and D
34. A and C
35. A and D
36. B and D
37. A and E
38. B and C
39. C
40. A
41. B
42. D
43. B
44. 31
45. 20
46. 19
47. 60
48. D
49. A
50. A
51. A
52. D
53. B
54. B
55. C
56. 1/4
57. 1/5
58. 4/9
59. 1/3
60. 4/5
61. 1/2
62. 1/3
63. 1/3
64. 17
65. 5
66. 4
67. 7
68. 14
69. 6
70. 2
71. 9
72. 1
73. 2
74. 5
75. 4

ANSWER TO TEST 05

1. C
2. D
3. C
4. B
5. B
6. B
7. D
8. C
9. B
10. D
11. D
12. C
13. C
14. C
15. B
16. D
17. 1/2
18. 3/7
19. 1/3
20. 1/3
21. 2/3
22. 3/4
23. B
24. A
25. D
26. C
27. A
28. C
29. D
30. B
31. D
32. B
33. C
34. 36
35. 48
36. 14
37. C and E
38. B and E
39. A and D
40. D and E
41. B and D
42. A and D
43. E
44. A
45. D
46. C
47. B
48. D
49. D
50. A
51. B
52. D
53. C
54. D
55. D
56. C
57. E
58. B
59. 36
60. 16
61. 275
62. 6
63. 23
64. 25
65. 5
66. 3
67. 18
68. 72
69. 40
70. 4
71. 7
72. 5
73. 4
74. 7
75. 4